endorsed for
BTEC

REVISE BTEC NATIONAL
Health and Social Care

REVISION
WORKBOOK

Series Consultant: Harry Smith

Authors: Brenda Baker, Elizabeth Haworth, James O'Leary
and Georgina Shaw

A note from the publisher

In order to ensure that this resource offers high-quality support for the associated Pearson qualification, it has been through a review process by the awarding body. This process confirms that this resource fully covers the teaching and learning content of the specification or part of a specification at which it is aimed. It also confirms that it demonstrates an appropriate balance between the development of subject skills, knowledge and understanding, in addition to preparation for assessment.

Endorsement does not cover any guidance on assessment activities or processes (e.g. practice questions or advice on how to answer assessment questions), included in the resource nor does it prescribe any particular approach to the teaching or delivery of a related course.

While the publishers have made every attempt to ensure that advice on the qualification and its assessment is accurate, the official specification and associated assessment guidance materials are the only authoritative source of information and should always be referred to for definitive guidance.

Pearson examiners have not contributed to any sections in this resource relevant to examination papers for which they had prior responsibility.

Examiners will not use endorsed resources as a source of material for any assessment set by Pearson.

Endorsement of a resource does not mean that the resource is required to achieve this Pearson qualification, nor does it mean that it is the only suitable material available to support the qualification, and any resource lists produced by the awarding body shall include this and other appropriate resources.

For the full range of Pearson revision titles across KS2, KS3, GCSE, Functional Skills, AS/A Level and BTEC visit:
www.pearsonschools.co.uk/revise

Published by Pearson Education Limited, 80 Strand, London, WC2R 0RL.

www.pearsonschoolsandfecolleges.co.uk

Copies of official specifications for all Edexcel qualifications may be found on the website:
qualifications.pearson.com/

Text © Pearson Education Limited 2016
Typeset and illustrated by Kamae Design
Produced by Out of House Publishing
Cover illustration by Miriam Sturdee

The rights of Brenda Baker, Elizabeth Haworth, James O'Leary, Georgina Shaw to be identified as authors
of this work have been asserted by them in accordance with the Copyright, Designs and Patents Act 1988.

First published 2016

19 18 17 16
10 9 8 7 6 5 4 3 2

British Library Cataloguing in Publication Data
A catalogue record for this book is available from the British Library

ISBN 978 1 292 15031 4

Printed in the UK by Bell and Bain Ltd, Glasgow

Acknowledgements
We are grateful to the following for permission to reproduce copyright material:

Figures
Figure on page 79 from Interrelationships between Atopic Disorders in Children: A Meta-Analysis Based on ISAAC
Questionnaires, David H. J. Pols Jorien B. Wartna, Elvira I. van Alphen, Heleen Moed, Nadine Rasenberg, Patrick J. E.
Bindels, Arthur M. Bohnen Published: July 2, 2015 http://dx.doi.org/10.1371/journal.pone.0131869

Text
Article on page 98 from Targeted case finding for chronic obstructive pulmonary disease versus routine practice in
primary care (TargetCOPD): a cluster-randomised controlled trial,18 July 2016, National Institute for Health Research,
contains public sector information licensed under the Open Government Licence v3.0; Link on page 106 and page
107 from Children's body max index, overweight and obesity, HSE 2014: Vol 1 Chapter 10 contains public sector
information licensed under the Open Government Licence v3.0; Article on page 129 from Cheap Alzheimer's drug
'may help keep people out of care homes', NHS Choices, contains public sector information licensed under the Open
Government Licence v3.0.

The publisher would like to thank the following for their kind permission to reproduce their photographs:

Fotolia.com: olegmalyshev (page 3)

All other images © Pearson Education

A note from the publisher
In order to ensure that this resource offers high-quality support for the associated Pearson qualification, it has been
through a review process by the awarding body. This process confirms that this resource fully covers the teaching
and learning content of the specification or part of a specification at which it is aimed. It also confirms that it
demonstrates an appropriate balance between the development of subject skills, knowledge and understanding, in
addition to preparation for assessment.

Endorsement does not cover any guidance on assessment activities or processes (e.g. practice questions or advice
on how to answer assessment questions), included in the resource nor does it prescribe any particular approach to
the teaching or delivery of a related course.

While the publishers have made every attempt to ensure that advice on the qualification and its assessment is
accurate, the official specification and associated assessment guidance materials are the only authoritative source of
information and should always be referred to for definitive guidance.

Pearson examiners have not contributed to any sections in this resource relevant to examination papers for which
they have responsibility.

Examiners will not use endorsed resources as a source of material for any assessment set by Pearson.

Endorsement of a resource does not mean that the resource is required to achieve this Pearson qualification,
nor does it mean that it is the only suitable material available to support the qualification, and any resource lists
produced by the awarding body shall include this and other appropriate resources.

123412

Revise BTEC National Health and Social Care Revision Workbook
ISBN 9781292150314
IMPORTANT ASSESSMENT UPDATE

As a result of feedback from the Department for Education, there have been some updates to the Set Task for **Unit 4 of BTEC Nationals in Health and Social Care**.

These updates mean there are now some changes required to this book. You need to be aware of this when using this book for revision.

PLEASE DO NOT USE PAGES 96–141 (Unit 4) OF THIS BOOK

We have provided updated versions of these pages for Unit 4, with answers, on the following website: www.pearsonfe.co.uk/BTECchanges

Changes to assessment of Unit 4: Enquiries into Current Research in Health and Social Care
Part A will be issued **4 weeks** ahead of Part B (instead of 6 weeks).
Part B must be completed in three hours in a **single session** (instead of over three days).
Your Part A notes to take into Part B (your supervised assessment period)   **May** include facts and figures relating to: • at least two other secondary sources covering the same area of research   • the research methods used   • data relating to research samples and results.   **Must not** include any conclusions drawn about: • the reliability of the research methods used   • the importance of the research   • implications of the research for practitioners and the sector   • plans for future research.

 Pearson

Introduction

This Workbook has been designed to support you in preparing for the externally assessed units of your course. Remember that you won't necessarily be studying all the units included here – it will depend on the qualification you are taking.

BTEC National Qualification	Externally assessed units
Certificate	1 Human Lifespan Development
For both: Extended Certificate Foundation Diploma	1 Human Lifespan Development 2 Working in Health and Social Care
Diploma	1 Human Lifespan Development 2 Working in Health and Social Care 4 Enquiries into Current Research in Health and Social Care
For both: Extended Diploma Extended Diploma (HS)	1 Human Lifespan Development 2 Working in Health and Social Care 3 Anatomy and Physiology for Health and Social Care 4 Enquiries into Current Research in Health and Social Care

Your Workbook

Each unit in this Workbook contains either one or two sets of revision questions or revision tasks, similar to those you will be set for your actual assessment. Working through these will help you to become familiar with the way in which you will be assessed and to develop the skills you require.

This Workbook will often include one or more useful features that explain or break down longer questions or tasks. Remember that these features won't appear in your actual assessment!

Grey boxes like this contain **hints and tips** about how to complete a task, interpret a brief, understand a concept or structure your responses.

 This icon will appear next to a **partial sample answer** to a question or task outcome. You should read the partial answer carefully, then complete it in your own words.

 This is a revision activity. It won't be one of the outcomes you need to produce in your actual assessment, but it will help you understand the processes you will need to go through.

 These boxes will tell you where you can find more help in Pearson's BTEC National Revision Guide. Visit **www.pearsonschools.co.uk/revise** for more information.

There is often space on the pages for you to write in. However, if you are carrying out research and making ongoing notes, you may want to use separate paper. Similarly, some units will be assessed through submission of digital files, or on screen, rather than on paper. Make sure you read the guidance for each unit that is given to you by Pearson and your teacher.

Contents

Unit 1: Human Lifespan Development

Your exam

You will have **1 hour 30 minutes** to complete your Unit 1 exam paper. You need to answer **every question** in the spaces provided. The paper is worth **90 marks** in total. The maximum number of marks available for each question indicates the amount of time you should spend on that question. When in your exam:

- use **correct spelling, punctuation and grammar**
- use a pen that writes in **black ink** and make sure you also have a spare pen with you.

Your exam questions

All the questions in your exam will relate to members of **one family**. As you work through the exam you will gradually find out more about each person so that you can answer questions about their development. Information will include details such as their:

- age
- relationships
- lifestyle choices
- environment
- life events.

In the second half of the exam paper, you will be given an **extended case study** relating to one member of the family. Case studies are used so that you can apply your knowledge and understanding of the content of this unit to **realistic situations** and **contexts**.

You should always read the case studies carefully, and apply knowledge and understanding about:

- key features of development across the life stages
- factors that impact on human growth and development
- theories that help to explain human growth and development
- life events that can impact on human growth and development
- the effects of ageing on the individual and on society.

You will be asked the following types of questions. There is guidance for each in this Workbook:

- Which
- Identify
- Explain
- Outline
- Describe
- Discuss
- Evaluate
- Justify
- To what extent

> **Links** To help you revise for your Unit 1 exam, this Workbook contains two full sets of revision papers starting on pages 2 and 15. See the introduction on page iii for more information on features included in the Workbook that will help you revise.

Revision paper 1

> **Answer ALL questions. Write your answers in the spaces provided.**

All questions relate to one family.

Guided 1 | Jan is 48 years of age. He has two children. Oscar is 8 years old and Anna is 18 months old. Anna is meeting the expected developmental milestones for her age.

Explain **two** possible features of Anna's physical development at her life stage. **4 marks**

> **'Explain'** questions are worth **up to 6 marks**. In these questions you must show that you **understand** the topic and give **reasons to support** your answer. You may be told how many features or types of feature you must explain.

1 Anna will be able to ....

....

....

because she will have developed the muscles in her back and legs.

2 Anna will be able to ....

....

....

because she has developed control in the small muscles of her hands and fingers.

> **Links** See pages 3–4 of the Revision Guide to revise development of gross and fine motor skills.

Total for Question 1 = 4 marks

2 | This is a photograph of Anna.

Which area of development is featured in the photograph of Anna?

1 mark

....

- You will need to relate your knowledge and understanding of development to members of the family described in case studies throughout your exam.
- **PIES** helps you to remember each of the areas of development: **P**hysical, **I**ntellectual, **E**motional, **S**ocial.
- 'Which' questions require you to quickly recall facts or features relating to human development. 'Which' questions range from 1 to 6 marks. For questions worth **1 mark** your answers need to be **brief**.

 Links See page 2 of the Revision Guide to revise areas of development.

Total for Question 2 = 1 mark

Guided

3 Oscar is doing well in mathematics at his local primary school.

Describe Oscar's intellectual development with reference to Piaget's theories of how children think and learn. **6 marks**

- Piaget carried out observations of children to show how they begin to think logically from the age of 7, and to show that they begin to see things from others' viewpoints.
- **'Describe'** questions range from **1 to 6 marks**. You must give a **clear account** that shows knowledge of the **facts** and **main features** of the topic.

According to Piaget's stages of development, at 8 years old Oscar is in the concrete operations stage. He will still need concrete apparatus such as counters to help him to work out problems but Oscar will now be able to conserve. This means ....

....

....

Piaget believed that, until the age of 7, children are egocentric. This means that Oscar will ....

....

Now that Oscar is 8, he will be able to ....

....

....

Links See page 11 of the Revision Guide to revise Piaget's observations on how children think.

Total for Question 3 = 6 marks

Guided   4   Jan's partner Lena died 10 months ago.

Discuss the likely negative effects of Lena's death on Jan's development.

10 marks

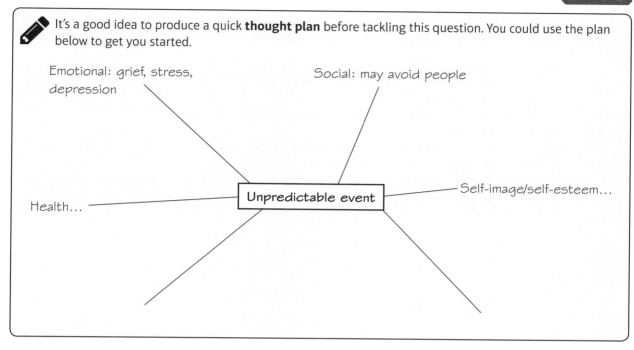

It's a good idea to produce a quick **thought plan** before tackling this question. You could use the plan below to get you started.

Emotional: grief, stress, depression

Social: may avoid people

Unpredictable event

Self-image/self-esteem...

Health...

The death of a partner is an unpredictable event that can cause a high level of stress. Stress is likely to have affected all aspects of Jan's development. Emotionally, Jan will be grieving and feeling upset. This can result in trauma that impacts on how he feels about himself, lowering his self-image and self-esteem and affecting his confidence to make decisions. Socially, Jan might feel uncomfortable meeting other people without Lena and so may avoid social events. His health may suffer because ...

....

....

....

....

....

....

....

....

....

....

Go on to discuss how Jan's physical and mental health might suffer. Think about how he may be affected and link this to the possible impact. For instance, he may have difficulty sleeping, be unable to eat or have a poor diet and generally not care for himself. Discuss how stress affects the heart. Conclude by discussing the possible impact on his psychological development and link your ideas to the Holmes-Rahe social adjustment rating scale.

Links   See page 30 of the Revision Guide to revise the Holmes-Rahe social adjustment rating scale.

Total for Question 4 = 10 marks

5   Jan has been Anna's main caregiver since she was born, and has formed a strong bond with her. Anna will be starting nursery soon and Jan is worried that she may not want to stay at the nursery without him.

Outline the importance of the development of a strong attachment between Anna and Jan before she starts nursery, with reference to theories of attachment.

6 marks

- **Attachment** describes the ability of the infant to bond with the person who is their main carer. Bowlby believed that a strong attachment with a child's main carer is important for their ability to form positive attachments as they get older. You need to provide information about the importance to a child of a strong attachment to the main caregiver.
- Show that you have referred to the case study by outlining the importance of Anna's attachment to Jan for developing future attachments with her carers at the nursery.
- 'Outline' questions are worth **up to 6 marks.** You need to give a **summary or overview** of the topic, or a **brief description.**

....

....

....

....

....

....

....

....

....

....

....

Links See page 13 of the Revision Guide to revise Bowlby and his theory of attachment.

Total for Question 5 = 6 marks

> **Guided**

6

> Jan was made redundant from his job and was unemployed for several months, which caused him anxiety and put a strain on the family's finances. He has now been offered a new, well-paid job in management.

Justify how the change in Jan's employment status and financial situation may impact on the development and wellbeing of the family.

`10 marks`

> In '**justify**' questions you need to give **valid reasons** for your answers and/or **prove** that something is right or reasonable. You need to give a **supported reason** for each point you make.
>
> 'Justify' questions may be short-answer questions ranging from **1 to 6 marks**, where you are required to show understanding of a topic, or long-answer questions ranging from **10 to 12 marks**, where you must make connections.

Being employed and having more income will impact on all areas of Jan's development. Emotionally, he

will..

....

....

....

His social development will be promoted because he will have more opportunity to

....

....

Intellectually, he ....

....

....

Physically, ...

....

....

An improvement in Jan's development and wellbeing will also affect the children's development and

wellbeing because ....

....

....

....

> **Links** See pages 28–30 of the Revision Guide to revise economic factors and the effects of life events.

Total for Question 6 = 10 marks

Guided

7 Oscar has experienced bullying at school.

Outline how bullying may affect Oscar's emotional development.

6 marks

> Bullying can cause physical injury and affect intellectual development. Notice that this question asks about the effects on **emotional** development only, so focus your answer on the question asked.

Bullying is likely to make Oscar feel isolated. This will impact on his self-image and lower his ....

....

It can cause him to become frightened and anxious, which can lead to ....

....

If bullying continues, it can have more serious effects on emotional development, leading to ....

....

....

In the long term, bullying could lead to Oscar ....

....

....

....

⌘ Links See page 26 of the Revision Guide to revise bullying and its effect on emotional development.

Total for Question 7 = 6 marks

8 | Anna's growth and development are being monitored by a health visitor.

Discuss the importance of monitoring Anna's growth and development, with reference to centiles and maturation theory.

`10 marks`

- **'Discuss'** questions require you to explore the topic in some **detail**. The amount of detail will be indicated by the number of marks available for the answer.
- **'Discuss'** questions may require **short answers** or **long answers**. The marks depend on the complexity of the question. Short-answer questions ranging from **1 to 6 marks** will require you to discuss straightforward information. Long-answer questions ranging from **10–12 marks** will require you to discuss more complex topics.
- To discuss, you need to show a **clear understanding** of the topic, consider all aspects of the topic and **balance your argument**, make **connections** between different aspects and discuss the **extent** or **importance** of features.

The health visitor will measure Anna's height and weight and check these against centiles that show the average for girls of Anna's age. He or she will plot this on a .... If Anna is growing more slowly or quickly than expected, the health visitor will ....

....

Maturation theory was developed by observing the abilities and skills of large numbers of children at different ages. The information was used to determine norms called .... that children will reach at a given age. The health visitor can apply them when she or he ....

....

The health visitor can use the information from the assessments to ....

....

....

Using information that shows the expected norms for children is important because it will enable the health visitor to ....

....

....

Links See pages 1–2 of the Revision Guide to revise principles of growth and development, and page 18 to revise maturation theory.

Total for Question 8 = 10 marks

9 | The family lives in a small village. A quarry has just opened nearby. This means that heavy lorries constantly pass the family's house, which is close to the road.

Outline the possible effects of the quarry on the family's health and wellbeing.

6 marks

- Write a sentence to outline how the quarry will have an impact on the environment.
- Write two sentences about the possible effects on health – think particularly about respiratory problems.
- Write a sentence or two about how it may make existing health problems worse and/or affect predispositions to illness.
- Write a sentence about the possible effects on wellbeing, thinking in particular about emotional effects.

....
....
....
....
....
....
....
....
....
....

Links | See page 23 of the Revision Guide to revise environmental factors affecting human growth and development.

Total for Question 9 = 6 marks

10 Jan's mother Gita is 73 years old and lives alone. When she was 50 she divorced her husband of 26 years. Shortly after, Gita found a lump in her breast which was cancerous. After undergoing surgery and chemotherapy she was given the all clear.

Gita had two children – Jan and his older sister Mela. Mela also developed breast cancer and died eight years ago when she was only 42 years old. This hit Gita hard and for a while she did not go out and lost interest in her hobbies and leisure activities. Jan became worried about his mother because for several years she was not eating regularly and used sleeping pills. Gita already smoked but she started smoking even more. Jan was particularly concerned because his grandfather, Gita's father, had had a mental illness and had committed suicide. Eventually, Jan persuaded Gita to go to her GP and she was diagnosed with depression. The GP gave her medication but also suggested a programme of exercise, which she followed.

Gita retired at 60. She had worked in an accounts office at an engineering factory for a number of years. Because she had worked part-time she did not receive a full pension and has had difficulties in making ends meet. She now claims pension credit and housing benefit, which has improved her finances.

At the age of 68, Gita's mental health showed improvement and she was encouraged to meet up with friends to go for walks and visit the cinema. For the last few years she has been eating more healthily and found that she no longer needed to take sleeping tablets. She also got help to stop smoking. Gita was asked to help at her local charity shop and soon found herself working there regularly. More recently, Gita has helped to care for Oscar after school by collecting him from school and taking him home.

Identify **three** services that may have supported Gita in later adulthood.

`3 marks`

- Think of services that may have supported Gita's mental health, helped her to stop smoking and helped her with her welfare needs.
- '**Identify**' questions require you to quickly recall facts or features relating to human development. '**Identify**' questions range between **3 and 6 marks**. Your answers need to be **brief**.

1 ....

2 ....

3 ....

 Links See page 39 of the Revision Guide to revise provision for the aged.

Total for Question 10 = 3 marks

11 Evaluate the importance of Gita maintaining a healthy lifestyle in her life stage.

`10 marks`

> 'Evaluate' questions always require **extended answers** and range from **10 to 12 marks.** To answer 'evaluate' questions you must consider **strengths and weaknesses**, **advantages and disadvantages** and the **relevance** or **significance** of, for example, a theory, factor or life event.

In later adulthood, as a normal part of ageing, individuals will usually notice a decline in the functions

of their body. Cardiovascular disease becomes more common because of raised cholesterol or high

blood pressure. Other diseases that are linked to ageing are ....

....

....

Poor lifestyle choices are likely to ....

....

....

....

A healthy lifestyle is important because ....

....

....

....

Although changes in lifestyle choices will not prevent some decline in ageing, they can help to ....

....

A healthy lifestyle is particularly important for Gita at her life stage because ....

....

....

....

> **Links** See pages 31–36 of the Revision Guide to revise illness and health in ageing.

Total for Question 11 = 10 marks

> **Guided**

12 Give **two** examples of the economic effects of an ageing population. Explain how each one affects the economy.

[6 marks]

1 An ageing population means a higher demand on ....

....

This may ....

....

2 An ageing population means an increase in the ratio of retired people to working people. This

means higher numbers of retirees claiming ....

This results in ....

....

Links See page 40 of the Revision Guide to revise the economic effects of an ageing population.

Total for Question 12 = 6 marks

13 To what extent does the nature versus nurture debate help to explain Gita's health and development?

12 marks

> Your answer could be structured as three paragraphs:
> - **Paragraph 1:** Use information about Gita's family history to explore any predisposition or susceptibility she may have to the physical and mental illnesses she has experienced.
> - **Paragraph 2:** Use the information about Gita's life events and her lifestyle to explore the impact they may have had on her health and development.
> - **Paragraph 3:** Discuss the extent of Gita's likely predisposition or susceptibility to illness and the extent to which stress associated with life events may have affected her development. Refer to the stress–diathesis model and Holmes-Rahe social adjustment rating scale to reach a **supported conclusion**.
>
> In '**to what extent' questions** you must provide **details** and give clear **evidence to support** your ideas. The question asks about the level or degree of something. The number of marks will depend on the difficulty of the topic. They may be **short-answer or long-answer questions**. In long-answer questions you will need to show how you have reached your conclusions.

....

....

....

....

....

....

....

....

....

....

....

....

....

....

....

Links See page 20 of the Revision Guide to revise the stress–diathesis model and page 30 to revise the Holmes-Rahe social adjustment rating scale.

Total for Question 13 = 12 marks

END OF PAPER 1   **TOTAL FOR PAPER = 90 MARKS**

Revision paper 2

Answer ALL questions. Write your answers in the spaces provided.

All questions relate to one family.

1 Arlene is 35 years old. She has a son, Kai, who is 12 years old, and a daughter, Shona, aged 4. Shona is starting school in September.

Discuss how Shona's fine motor skills will help her independence when she starts school. **6 marks**

You need to recall the milestones for fine motor skills reached at 4 years old and use your knowledge of the types of activity Shona will take part in at school, including independent personal care.

....
....
....
....
....
....
....
....
....
....
....
....
....

Links See page 4 of the Revision Guide to revise the development of fine motor skills.

Total for Question 1 = 6 marks

2 | Kai has experienced peer pressure at school from his friendship group.

Identify **three negative** features of behaviour that may be caused by peer pressure. | 3 marks

1 ....

2 ....

3 ....

🔗 **Links** See pages 14 and 16 of the Revision Guide to revise self-concept, friendships and relationships. See page 17 of the Revision Guide to revise peer pressure.

Total for Question 2 = 3 marks

3 | Arlene has just found out that she is expecting another baby in seven months' time. Arlene smokes and likes to drink wine in the evening after work.

Explain, giving **two** examples, the possible effects of Arlene's lifestyle on her baby's development. | 6 marks

1 ....

....

....

....

....

2 ....

....

....

....

....

🔗 **Links** See page 22 of the Revision Guide to revise biological factors that affect development.

Total for Question 3 = 6 marks

4 Arlene has noticed that Shona often copies her brother's behaviour.

Discuss the importance of **positive** role models with reference to Bandura's social learning theory.

10 marks

Remember not to confuse negative reinforcement with punishment. When discussing how Shona may repeat the learned behaviour, remember that negative reinforcement encourages repeated behaviour because of the **removal** of something. For example, Shona puts her toys away because she has seen her brother tidying up. Her mother stops nagging her so she repeats the behaviour because the negative consequence has been removed.

....

....

....

....

....

....

....

....

....

....

....

....

....

....

....

....

....

Links See page 19 of the Revision Guide to revise Bandura's social learning theory.

Total for Question 4 = 10 marks

5 Shona's new school provides children with time for free play to explore a range of natural materials that they can use in construction activities and artwork. There are areas with resources for imaginative and role play, and a natural outdoor area.

In the context of Piaget's theories of cognitive development, justify free play provision for the children.

10 marks

You need to make clear links between experience-based activities and Piaget's theory of how children develop their thought processes by accommodating their new experiences.

....

....

....

....

....

....

....

....

....

....

....

....

....

....

....

....

....

....

....

Links See page 10 of the Revision Guide to revise Piaget's stages of cognitive development and Schematic Development Theory.

Total for Question 5 = 10 marks

6 Kai is in the adolescent life stage. Arlene has been speaking to him about the physical changes he will experience during puberty.

Describe the physical changes Kai will experience during puberty.　**6 marks**

Balance your answer by including information about primary and secondary sexual characteristics.

....
....
....
....
....
....
....
....

Links See page 5 of the Revision Guide to revise physical development during adolescence.

Total for Question 6 = 6 marks

7 Arlene has a younger brother, Mike, aged 21.

Explain Mike's development at his life stage, giving **two** examples.　**4 marks**

Mike is in the early adult stage, when individuals are fully grown. Try to give examples relating to two different aspects of Mike's development.

1 ....
....
....
....
2 ....
....
....
....

Links See pages 6, 9 and 17 of the Revision Guide to revise development in early adulthood.

Total for Question 7 = 4 marks

8 Arlene split up with her partner, Jermaine, three months ago.

Outline how the breakdown in Arlene's relationship may have affected her emotional and social development.

6 marks

....

....

....

....

....

....

....

....

....

....

Links See pages 29–30 of the Revision Guide to revise the effect of life events.

Total for Question 8 = 6 marks

9 Arlene's mother, Sofia, is 56 years old. Sofia lives with her partner, Clive, and works as a nurse at the local hospital. Sofia has started the menopause.

Discuss possible **positive** and **negative** effects of Sofia's life stage on her health and development.

10 marks

Remember, you need to discuss possible **positive** and **negative** effects of this life stage. Middle adulthood can bring more financial security if the person is in work and any children have left home. Think about the impact of economic factors on a person's development.

In middle adulthood Sofia may begin a gradual decline in physical health and we know that she has started the menopause. What negative effects might Sofia notice?

....

....

....

....

....

....

....

....

....

....

....

....

....

....

....

....

Links See page 7 of the Revision Guide to revise physical development in middle adulthood, page 17 for the development of independence through the life stages, and page 28 to revise economic factors.

Total for Question 9 = 10 marks

10 | Arlene's grandmother, Mary, is 79 years old. Mary has been living alone for many years and until recently was very active. She attended her local church regularly and had many friends there. She was able to catch the bus to the local town where she did her own shopping. Arlene and her mum, Sofia, went to see Mary each week and offered to help, but Mary likes to be independent and always refused.

Mary worked in her local supermarket for many years and retired at the age of 60. It took her a while to get used to not having a job. She particularly missed her colleagues and customers. Through her church she found a local charity shop and started to help out two mornings a week. Although she was now getting more tired and had arthritis and some hearing loss, Mary felt fairly healthy and continued with voluntary work one morning each week, until last year when she had a fall and broke her hip.

Mary spent two months in hospital. When she was discharged she was assessed by a social worker who was concerned that, although she could manage to wash, dress and make light meals, she would not be able to carry out all day-to-day activities. A care plan was agreed and Mary now has a carer who attends her each day to help her with chores. She has hot meals delivered and her daughter, Sofia, visits each week to help with shopping and cleaning. Community services have provided a stairlift and she has a walking frame.

Sofia is getting increasingly worried about Mary. Although Mary has had some physiotherapy and can now walk short distances with the walking frame, she doesn't use it much and hasn't attempted to get out. Sometimes Sofia finds that Mary has not eaten her food. The house often feels cold, but Mary will not turn up the heating, saying that she puts on extra clothing and goes to bed early instead. Mary did have a friend from church who she saw regularly, but she died recently. Sofia often suggests taking Mary out to go to church or visit other friends, but Mary always makes an excuse, saying that she's too tired or that it's too cold out. In the past, Mary always took care with her appearance, but often now doesn't bother to comb her hair. Sofia has suggested that Mary moves into residential accommodation, but each time she mentions it Mary gets very angry.

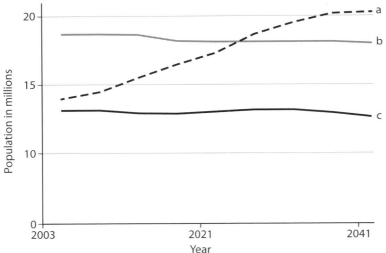

Predicted population changes for under 16s, under 25s and over 60s

Which line on the graph indicates the predicted changes in population of people over 60 years old?

1 mark

....

Links See page 40 of the Revision Guide to revise ageing and economic effects.

Total for Question 10 = 1 mark

11 Discuss Mary's development in the years after her retirement in relation to theories of ageing.

10 marks

....

....

....

....

....

....

....

....

....

....

....

....

....

Links See page 38 of the Revision Guide to revise theories of ageing.

Total for Question 11 = 10 marks

12 Outline why there is an increased risk of falls for older people, with reference to the physical changes in ageing.

6 marks

> Falls can be the result of many conditions of ageing. Discuss a range of conditions to explore how they may affect mobility, orientation and balance.

....
....
....
....
....
....
....
....

> **Links** See pages 8 and 31–35 of the Revision Guide to revise conditions of ageing. See page 36 for the effects of illness common in ageing.

Total for Question 12 = 6 marks

13 To what extent is Mary's fall likely to have affected her development and wellbeing?

12 marks

....

....

....

....

....

....

....

....

....

....

....

....

....

....

....

....

....

....

....

....

....

....

....

....

....

....

Links See pages 8 and 31–35 of the Revision Guide to revise conditions of ageing. See page 36 to revise the effects of illnesses common in ageing, and page 37 for the psychological effects of ageing

Total for Question 13 = 12 marks

END OF PAPER 2   **TOTAL FOR PAPER = 90 MARKS**

Unit 2: Working in Health and Social Care

Your exam

You will have **1 hour 30 minutes** to complete your Unit 2 exam paper. You need to answer **every question** in the spaces provided. The paper is worth **80 marks** in total. The maximum number of marks available for each question indicates the amount of time you should spend on that question.

When in your exam:
- use **correct spelling, punctuation and grammar**
- use a pen that writes in **black ink** and make sure you also have a spare pen with you.

Your exam questions

Your exam paper is divided into four sections: A, B, C and D. Each section is worth a total of 20 marks and you have just over 20 minutes to answer each section. Each section is based on a different short **scenario** that briefly explains the situation of a person with health and social care needs. It may cover:
- ill health
- learning disabilities
- physical and sensory disabilities
- age-related needs.

Scenarios are used so that you can apply your knowledge and understanding of the content of this unit to **realistic situations** and **contexts**.

You should always read the scenarios carefully, and apply knowledge and understanding about:
- the specific needs of different groups of service users
- how different health and social care workers can work together to meet these needs
- roles and responsibilities of different workers
- the regulation of workers, working practices and organisations in health and social care.

Each section contains four questions that ask you to:
- identify *or* outline (2 marks)
- describe (4 marks)
- explain (6 marks)
- discuss (8 marks).

You will find guidance on these question types in this Workbook and also in the Revision Guide.

 Links To help you revise for your Unit 2 exam, this Workbook contains two full revision papers starting on pages 27 and 43. See the introduction on page iii for more information on features that help you revise.

Revision paper 1

1

Scenario 1: Ill health

Carlos is 19 and is studying at a university in the town where he lives. His parents and friends are very concerned about the amount of weight he has lost over the past year. Carlos is unwilling to talk about the situation.

During a lecture, Carlos collapses and is taken to the health centre on the university campus where he is seen by a nurse. She asks him about his weight loss and he discusses the reasons for it with her. His height is 175 cm. He weighs 50 kg and his body mass index (BMI) is 16.3.

Carlos attends an appointment with his GP, who refers him to a specialist service for people with eating disorders. The service also provides support to enable people like Carlos to manage their mental health.

During conversations with specialist staff at the service, Carlos reveals that the reason for his weight loss is linked to his fear about telling other people that he is gay.

Scenario 1 is about someone who has ill health. The example above is about Carlos, who has an eating disorder.

Read the scenario thoroughly to get a picture of the setting. This will give you an overview of
* the service user (Carlos)
* his needs
* the health and social care staff who support him.

(a) Identify **two** signs that the nurse at the health centre might look for when asking Carlos about his medical situation.

2 marks

'Identify' questions need **short**, **factual** answers.

1   Whether Carlos is trying to disguise his weight loss.

2   Whether Carlos wants to keep control of personal information such as weight loss so does not

want to be ....

Instead of being asked an 'identify' question, you may be asked an 'outline' question. Answering an 'outline' question involves an overview, where you give a brief outline of the topic and may give a linked response.

For example: Outline the role of external agencies in inspecting health and social care services. (2 marks) An answer could be: Inspection to monitor and grade against national standards and benchmarks.

Links See page 106 of the Revision Guide for help on answering 'identify' and 'outline' questions.

Guided ⟩

(b) Describe **two** ways that staff at the specialist services might support Carlos when he is referred there by his GP.

4 marks

1 The staff might explain to Carlos about eating disorders, the type of disorder he has and the effects which it could have on him, such as psychological, emotional and physical effects.

2 The staff might ask Carlos questions about his lifestyle, such as ....

....

....

- It is useful to **refer back to the scenario**, so that you take into account any information that relates to the question. Make sure that you note the **key words** in the **scenario** and in the **question**. For example, in Question 1(b), note the word 'staff' (because you have to say what they do) and 'support' (because you have to say how they provide it).
- To answer the question, you must give **two ways** and then add more detail to each one. One way has been completed as an example. **First,** you should state one way the staff at the specialist services might support Carlos (e.g. by explaining about eating disorders and the type of disorder he has). You will recall this from your knowledge about what staff, including nurses, at specialist services do. **Then** you should add another statement which develops and clarifies the point (e.g. explaining about the different kinds of effects on Carlos).

🔗 **Links** Questions 1(a) and 1(b) focus on the responsibilities of people who work in health and social care settings. Look at pages 56–61 of the Revision Guide to revise these, and page 107 for help with answering 'describe' questions.

Guided ⟩

(c) Explain reasons why people might not access the health and social care services they need.

6 marks

One of the main barriers to accessing health and social care services is the unwillingness of people to seek help when they need it. This can be the case with people who have mental ill health, which is sometimes the cause of eating disorders.

This question asks you to **explain**, which means that you need to answer in more **detail**. The example here makes a good first point, with supporting reasons, about the link between mental ill health and eating disorders. Make your own point **linked** to **supporting reasons** in the space provided. For example, suggest why Carlos does not want to access the services he needs. What is he worried about? You will find this information in the last sentence in the scenario.

In the case of Carlos, a reason might be ....

....

Your second point, **linked with supporting reasons,** could be about a different person who might not access services they need. When you develop your answer in this way, and make a further point about another kind of service user, you are showing that you can apply your knowledge in different ways and that you can think of relevant points that are not in the scenario, for example:

A further reason might be that people cannot afford it. ....

....

....

Add a sentence to **explain** and **develop** the point, for example, mentioning the cost of travel to the service or the cost of the service itself. Make a **relevant link**.

> The points made so far are about access to **healthcare**. Instead of the second point above, you could make a point about **social care**, for example:

A reason people might not access social care services is because they will have to pay for them. For example, older people may need residential care but don't want to use their savings to pay for their care.

> You could finish with a brief **conclusion**, summing up your **overall response**, like the one below:

In conclusion, some of the main reasons why people do not access the health and social care services they need might be related to mental health, being worried about something (e.g. reluctant to disclose sexuality) or financial concerns.

Others may not access services because ....

....

....

....

....

> You could add a brief final sentence to the conclusion that shows your wider knowledge. For example, you could mention cultural reasons (such as worry about taking clothes off), geographical reasons (such as difficulty in reaching the services) or a lack of knowledge (for example, because they don't know about them).

> **Links** The question focuses on issues that affect access to services. Look at page 84 of the Revision Guide to revise barriers to accessing health and social care, and page 108 for help with answering 'explain' questions.

> **Guided**

(d) Discuss ways that health and social care staff could empower Carlos to continue to improve his health after his specialist care has finished.

8 marks

It is a priority that Carlos continues his recovery and maintains good mental and physical health. Health and social care staff might provide him with a healthy eating plan that is monitored by members of his family and by the support staff carrying out regular checks during future appointments. The staff also need to put in place measures which will prevent the likelihood of a relapse, so their proposals need to be agreed with Carlos to meet his needs and preferences.

> This first paragraph ends with Carlos's needs and preferences. Using information from the scenario, continue the answer. For example, a positive way of empowering Carlos would be to encourage him to be proud of who he is rather than worrying about what other people think.

Carlos may feel that his most important need is ....

....

> The health and social care workers are trying to support Carlos. Next you should discuss what they might recommend to empower him.

....

....

....

....

In your next point, discuss another way that Carlos could be empowered and explain it.

....

....

....

....

- When adding your concluding sentences, remember the **key care values:** empowerment, respect, dignity and maintaining confidentiality (privacy).
- Make sure your conclusion refers back to the **key words** in the question. In this case, the key word is **'empower'** and the points made so far are about how Carlos will be empowered.
- Empowerment is a **key care value**. You could finish your conclusion with a point about how important it is for health and social care workers to apply care values when they work with vulnerable people like Carlos.

....

....

....

....

....

....

To write a strong answer:
- demonstrate **accurate** and **thorough knowledge** about empowering Carlos
- produce a **well-developed** and **balanced discussion**, showing a grasp of competing arguments and pros/cons in the context of Carlos's health and social care needs
- show **clear**, **logical reasoning**, using specialist technical language.

A good conclusion can strengthen your answer. For example, you could refer back to the key points of the question and briefly sum up your points.

⌯ Links Question 1(d) focuses on the specific responsibilities of people who work in health and social care settings, and also on empowering individuals. Look at pages 65–66 of the Revision Guide to revise how health and social care staff can empower individuals, page 70 for ensuring confidentiality, page 74 for holistic approaches and page 109 for help with answering 'discuss' questions.

Total for Question 1 = 20 marks

SECTION B

Answer ALL questions. Write your answers in the spaces provided.

Guided ▷ **2** | **Scenario 2: Learning disability**

Salome has a profound learning disability.

This means that, according to the Department of Health, she has a significantly reduced ability to

- understand new or complex information
- learn new skills
- cope independently.

Some people are born with a learning disability. Other people develop learning disabilities as a result of an accident or illness during childhood or later life.

Salome finds it very difficult to communicate. She has additional sensory needs, physical disabilities and mental ill health. Some of her behaviour is challenging. She sometimes makes her preferences known through her behaviour and her reactions.

Salome needs a wide range of support. This includes help with day-to-day needs, including dressing and toileting. She currently lives with her family and has trained specialist carers. These carers also enable her family to have respite.

Her carers are trying to find ways to enable Salome to be involved in decisions about her needs. They are working on different ways of communicating with her, based on techniques developed by the learning disability charity Mencap in their 'Involve Me' project.

Scenario 2 is about someone who has a learning disability. In the example above, you will see that it is about Salome who has a profound learning disability and other health and personal care needs. Read the scenario thoroughly to gain an overview of:
- the service user (Salome)
- her needs
- the health and social care staff who support her
- the involvement of her family.

(a) Apart from help with dressing and toileting, identify **two** of Salome's day-to-day needs. `2 marks`

You can work out these answers from the scenario. This tells you that Salome cannot learn new skills or cope independently. This means she cannot do tasks by herself. You will also recall knowledge from your learning about the needs of people who have a learning disability.

1 Help with feeding.

2 Help with ....

 Links Look at page 97 of the Revision Guide to revise caring for people with learning disabilities, and page 106 for help with answering 'identify' questions.

31

> Guided >

(b) Apart from providing respite, describe **two** ways that Salome's trained specialist carers support members of her family.

4 marks

> You can work out both ways from the point made in the scenario about Salome exhibiting challenging behaviour. One way is given as an example below. Complete the second way below.

1   The carers help family members to manage Salome when she exhibits challenging behaviour. They could show Salome's family some strategies which are designed to calm her down in these situations.

> • Always read the question carefully and answer the question you are asked. The question starts '**Apart** from providing respite', so don't give 'providing respite' as part of your answer!
> • For each of the two ways required, give a **statement** that describes a way in which the carers support members of Salome's family. You will recall this from your knowledge about what carers do. Then add another statement which **develops** each way and **clarifies** it, as shown in the example.
> • It is useful to **refer back to the scenario**, so that you take into account information that is relevant for each question. Make sure that you note the **key words** in the **scenario** and in the **question**. For example, in Question 2(b), note 'carers' (because you have to say what they do) and 'support' (because you have to say how they provide it).

2   The carers might also show family members ways to prevent Salome physically harming herself.

These ways could include ....

....

> **Links** Question 2(b) focuses on the responsibilities of people who work in health and social care settings, and on supporting the routines of service users. Look at pages 97–98 of the Revision Guide for caring for people with learning disability, and physical and sensory disability, and page 107 for help with answering 'describe' questions.

> Guided >

(c) Explain ways that health and social care workers support people with learning disabilities.

6 marks

Health and social care workers who support people with profound learning disabilities need skills which enable them to respond to, and manage, complex needs. As Salome has a range of other physical disabilities and mental ill health, staff need to be able to support these conditions and minimise their effects on Salome.

> This question asks you to **explain**, which means that you need to answer in more **detail**. As in the example above, first you must say what health and social care workers do when supporting people with learning disabilities. Next you should **link** and **develop your point** by recognising that Salome has a wide range of needs. Consider the care workers' need to understand which symptoms and behaviours are the result of a learning disability and which are not. You could develop the point by explaining how this might be done and any skills needed.
>
> When answering a question involving skills, think about ways that skills can be developed, such as training or continuing professional development, or through experience. Continue the answer on the lines below.

....

....

....

....

....

You will give a strong answer by including knowledge of the different types of skills that health and social care workers are required to have, as in the example below.

Staff also need to have communication skills that are effective when working with people who have mild or profound learning disabilities. They need to be able to recognise and interpret the meanings of certain behaviours and reactions, especially when they are challenging.

....

....

....

....

....

....

Notice the reference to an aspect of the scenario in this sample answer, about challenging behaviours and the skills needed to recognise and interpret them. Add another sentence to explain and develop this point. Use a relevant link. For example, one way would be to link to **key care values**.

Finish with a conclusion like the one below. You could write a sentence that sums up your overall response to the scenario in relation to specific needs and working practices. This sample conclusion also refers very clearly to key care values.

In conclusion, if support is given as explained above, it means that people such as Salome who have learning disabilities would have support that is tailored to their specific needs. Salome would have choice and control over the things that are important to her.

....

....

....

....

Add a concluding sentence relating to the key care values of dignity and respect.

Links The questions above are focused around caring for people with specific needs, and working practices. See pages 95–98 of the Revision Guide to revise specific needs, pages 102–103 for working practices and page 108 for help with answering 'explain' questions.

Guided (d) Discuss ways that people with any level of learning disability can be enabled to communicate their needs and preferences.

8 marks

Firstly, the most effective way to help people with a learning disability to communicate is through partnership working, by involving a range of people and organisations. These might include family members, frontline staff, advocates, service managers and people who plan and commission services.

To continue a **balanced discussion**, you could include what carers **should not** do and what they **should** do, following up your points with reasons. Continue the balanced discussion below. Link back to Salome in the scenario and how she could be enabled to communicate her needs and preferences.

To help people with learning disabilities, family members, frontline staff and advocates should not ......

....

....

....

....

> You could go on to develop your answer as follows.

One way that people with a learning disability can communicate their needs and preferences is by learning new skills. This would enable them to do something for themselves and so to communicate their own wishes. While Salome would find this very difficult, there are some basic skills, such as being able to wash her hands, that she could do from time to time. This could help her start to manage her frustration, benefit her mental health, and help introduce positive communication, resulting in less frequent challenging behaviour.

> Look at the points being made. They refer to the **scenario** – Salome finds learning new tasks difficult. The answer shows how, while this is true, there are some tasks which she could cope with, which would help introduce positive communication.

> Complete the conclusion below by discussing alternative methods of communication for people with a learning disability, such as the use of gestures or signs. Summarise the most important outcomes for people with learning disabilities, such as Salome. Refer to the **key values** of needs and preferences.

In conclusion, by helping people such as Salome to communicate their needs and preferences through

learning new skills such as ....

....

....

their quality of life might be improved.

> To write a strong answer:
> - demonstrate **accurate** and **thorough knowledge** of enabling people with a learning disability, such as Salome, to communicate their needs and preferences
> - produce a **well-developed** and **balanced** discussion, showing a grasp of competing arguments and pros and cons in the context of communication for people with a learning disability
> - show **clear**, **logical reasoning**, using specialist technical language.
>
> A good conclusion can strengthen your answer. For example, refer back to the key points of the question and briefly sum up your points.

> **Links** This question focuses on the specific responsibilities of people who work in health and social care settings – applying care values and promoting rights. Look at pages 60–61 of the Revision Guide to revise responsibilities, page 97 to revise supporting people with learning disabilities, page 101 to revise the protection and promotion of individual rights, and page 109 for help with answering 'discuss' questions.

Total for Question 2 = 20 marks

SECTION C

Answer ALL questions. Write your answers in the spaces provided.

Guided

3 | **Scenario 3: Physical/sensory disabilities**

Lars is 25. He was involved in an accident while rock climbing. After he received emergency medical care in a hospital, an orthopaedic surgeon (a doctor who treats injuries to bones and muscles) told Lars that he had broken his spine.

Lars now uses a wheelchair. He is able to lift himself in and out of his wheelchair and he uses it to get from one place to another, including from home to work.

He lives near a tram stop and the trams are accessible to people who use wheelchairs. He works in an office which is adapted to include accessible ramps, lifts, office furniture and canteen facilities.

Before his accident, Lars was active in a range of sports. He maintains this interest and now participates in different types of sports, including basketball, tennis and archery.

While Lars is not happy about having to spend a lot of time in his wheelchair, he has adapted successfully and continues to lead a full and meaningful life.

Scenario 3 is about someone who has a physical disability. The example above is about Lars, who has a physical disability, and how he has adapted to the changes in his life circumstances. Read the scenario thoroughly to get a picture of the setting. This will give you an overview of:
- the service user (Lars)
- his needs
- how he copes with his disability.

(a) Apart from the orthopaedic surgeon, identify **two** healthcare workers who would have been involved in providing care for Lars after his accident.

2 marks

Notice that the question starts 'Apart from the orthopaedic surgeon'. You will get no marks if you answer 'orthopaedic surgeon'. Read the question **carefully** and answer the question you are asked. To identify the second healthcare worker, think about who would help Lars with daily needs such as personal care.

1   Accident and emergency nurse.

2   ....

 Links   Look at pages 56 and 60 of the Revision Guide to revise roles and responsibilities of healthcare workers and page 106 for help with answering 'identify' questions.

Guided

(b) Describe **two** ways that healthcare workers would have enabled Lars to recover from his accident.

4 marks

- For each of the two ways required, give a **statement** that describes a way that healthcare workers would have enabled Lars to recover. You will recall this from your knowledge about what healthcare workers do. Then add another statement which **develops** each way and **clarifies** it.
- One way has been completed for you as an example.
- It is useful to refer back to the **scenario** so that you take into account information that is relevant to each question. Make sure that you note the **key words** in the scenario and the question. For example, in Question 3(b), note the word 'recover' – you might link this to rehabilitation because this is one aspect of recovery. Helping patients to recover is a key responsibility of healthcare workers, including ways to help Lars develop independence in coping with his practical everyday life, needs and activities.

1 A nurse would prepare a care plan for Lars. This would be likely to recommend that he has physiotherapy to help him build his muscle strength.

2 ....

....

....

....

Links Question 3(b) focuses on the responsibilities of people who work in healthcare settings, especially those connected with enabling rehabilitation. Look at pages 56 and 60 of the Revision Guide to revise healthcare roles and responsibilities and page 107 for help with answering 'describe' questions.

Guided

(c) Explain how hospitals, such as the one where Lars was treated after his accident, are inspected.

6 marks

This question asks you to **explain**, which means that you need to answer in more **detail**. As in the example below, you should start with a brief, direct statement showing that you know which organisation inspects hospitals.

Hospitals are inspected by staff from external organisations, such as the Care Quality Commission (CQC) in England.

When hospitals are inspected, the inspectors ask people who use the services provided by the hospital for their views, to find out whether they are satisfied with the ways they have been treated.

....

....

....

....

The answer goes on to focus clearly on **how** inspections are carried out, showing that the learner knows what happens during an inspection of a hospital. This question asks **how** but **not why**, so this focus is correct. Continue the answer with a sentence about how knowledge of service users' views might help the inspectors.

Below is another way that inspectors find out about the ways hospital staff provide care.

Inspectors also observe staff at the hospital providing care for patients.

> Add another sentence to **explain** and **develop** this point. Use a **relevant link**. For example, you could write a sentence about how inspectors also observe the way staff keep patient records and individual care plans, and whether these meet the needs and preferences of the patients.

....

....

> In your conclusion, you could explain what happens after the inspection is finished. This shows that you have a clear knowledge of the entire inspection process.

In conclusion, the findings of the inspection are published by the CQC and these can be read by people who want to know about the quality of the services provided.

> Add a further sentence about how a hospital and staff members might need to respond to the findings of the inspection, such as via improvement action plans, enhanced staff training, improved partnership working or changes to working practices that might involve cleanliness and hygiene.

....

....

> **Links** Question 3(c) focuses on the roles of organisations that inspect health and social care services, and how inspections are carried out. Look at page 76 of the Revision Guide to revise how care is monitored externally, pages 87–90 for the regulation and inspection process, and page 108 for help with answering 'explain' questions.

> **Guided**

(d) Discuss ways that people like Lars, who develop a physical disability, are enabled to come to terms with their condition.

8 marks

> • The example answer below describes how the surgeon helps people like Lars to come to terms with their condition by explaining the diagnosis, treatment, likely impact on the person and the support available from now on. You don't need to give details about the treatment. You are not an orthopaedic surgeon so you are not expected to know that!
> • Continue the answer by discussing how, as part of coming to terms with a physical disability, Lars will need to tell his family and friends, who will also need to come to terms with what has happened.

People like Lars will need help to deal with their diagnosis. The surgeon will tell Lars the outcome of the accident, explain what treatment is available, how likely it is to be successful, what he is likely to be able to do when he has recovered, and the support that will be put in place, such as physiotherapists, occupational therapists and counsellors.

....

....

> Go on to develop your point by showing how support from family and friends, as well as health and social care services, will enable Lars come to terms with his condition.

Family and friends will also help someone like Lars come to terms with his condition. For example,

....

....

....

....

One way to continue your answer is to consider not only coming to terms with physical disability, but also the emotional and psychological support that might be needed. You could use technical terms such as 'post-traumatic stress disorder' or, if you are unsure, use relevant general terms such as 'anxiety', 'fear' and 'depression'. Below is an example of a way to make this point and explain it.

The diagnosis of physical disability might also affect a person's mental health. If so, psychological services, such as counselling, could be used. For example, although Lars is very active after his accident, he might also experience post-traumatic stress disorder or other forms of anxiety. This might not affect him straight away but could be a long-term effect, and a counsellor could suggest strategies to help Lars deal with his anxiety.

Continue to discuss how someone like Lars might come to terms with his condition in contexts such as sport to improve his physical health or through accessible travel and workplaces. Consider some positive and negative aspects someone in Lars's situation might experience.

....

....

Finish with a conclusion. You could sum up your overall response by referring to a key care value and outcome for people like Lars – independence. The scenario tells you that Lars was very active before his accident and that he has recovered successfully to lead a meaningful life.

In conclusion, health and social care workers play key roles in helping people to come to terms with

and recover ....

....

To write a strong answer:
- demonstrate **accurate** and **thorough knowledge** of enabling people such as Lars, who have developed a physical disability, to come to terms with the condition
- produce a **well-developed** and **balanced** discussion in the context of developing a physical disability
- show **clear**, **logical** reasoning, using specialist technical language.

A good conclusion can strengthen your answer. For example, refer back to the key points of the question and briefly sum up your points.

Links This question focuses on the responsibilities of people who work in health and social care settings, particularly assessment, care and support planning, involving service users and their families, and working with people with specific needs. Look at pages 56–61 of the Revision Guide to revise roles and responsibilities, page 62 for supporting the routines of service users, page 98 for the care of people with physical and sensory disabilities, and page 109 for help with answering 'discuss' questions.

Total for Question 3 = 20 marks

SECTION D

Answer ALL questions. Write your answers in the spaces provided.

 4

Scenario 4: Age-related needs

Hal is 70. He was recently diagnosed with a brain tumour which his neurosurgeon told him is inoperable and that he had about six months to live.

Before his diagnosis, Hal was healthy except for failing eyesight. He would prefer to remain at home until he dies, in familiar surroundings. He has support from Marie Curie, a charity which provides care and support for people like Hal who have a terminal illness.

The Marie Curie nurse who supports Hal asks him about his needs and preferences, for example whether he wants members of his family to be involved in his care. She also advises Hal about palliative care. This is care which helps people to manage their pain levels.

Hal's condition gets worse and he talks to his Marie Curie nurse about going into a hospice where he can receive constant care. He dies on the day he is admitted to the hospice.

Scenario 4 is about someone with age-related needs. This example is about a person who has a terminal illness. Read the scenario thoroughly to give you an overview of:
- the service user (Hal)
- his needs and preferences
- the roles and responsibilities of the healthcare workers.

(a)   Identify **two** reasons why Hal might prefer to receive care at home.

2 marks

The example answer is about the place Hal prefers to receive care. Your second answer could be about people.

1   He will be in a familiar environment – a place he knows and recognises so he will know where everything is, as he can't see very well.

2   ....

....

 Links Look at page 82 of the Revision Guide to revise domiciliary care, page 80 for hospice care, and page 106 for help with answering 'identify' questions.

> **Guided**

(b) Describe **two** ways that the Marie Curie nurse will help Hal to manage his pain. | 4 marks |

> For each of the two ways required, give a **statement** that describes a way that the Marie Curie nurse can help Hal to manage his pain. You will recall this from your knowledge about what specialist nurses do. You should then add another statement which **develops** each way and **clarifies** it. One way has been completed for you as an example.
>
> It is useful to refer back to the scenario so that you take into account information that is relevant to each question. Make sure that you note the **key words** in the **scenario** and **question**. For example, in Question 4(b), note the key word 'nurse' – you have to remember the key responsibilities of people who work in health and social care settings. Helping patients to manage their pain is a key aspect of the role of a nurse.

1   The nurse will give Hal his medication. This will help him to manage the impact of his pain and have the best possible quality of life.

2   ....

....

> 🔗 **Links**   The questions focuses on the responsibilities of people who work in health and social care settings. Look at pages 56 and 60 of the Revision Guide for key roles and responsibilities in healthcare, and page 107 for help with answering 'describe' questions.

> **Guided**

(c) Explain why services such as hospice care might be provided in a variety of settings. | 6 marks |

> • This question asks you to **explain**, which means that you need to answer in more **detail**. In the example below, the learner shows knowledge of why services are provided in different settings and where hospice care is delivered. Pin it down right at the start!
> • To support the last point above, give a brief example of a type of care which is usually only provided in one setting.

Health and social care services are provided in different settings in order to meet the widest range of needs. Hospice care can be delivered in different settings, including in people's homes and residential care settings, but other types of health and social care can only be delivered in specific settings. ....

....

....

> The next point refers back to the service user, Hal. You are showing why he is having care in a specific setting, his home.

Because Hal prefers to remain in his own home, the Marie Curie nurse provides care there.

....   > Add another sentence to develop this point. Use a **relevant link**. For example, one way would be to link individual preferences to places where services are provided so that individual needs are met.

....

....

....

....

Complete the conclusion below to show that you understand that it is not only patient needs which determine where services are provided.

Finally, providing services in different settings can be cost effective. For example, ...

....

....

....

Links Question 4(c) focuses on settings where health and social care services are provided to meet different needs. Look at pages 57 and 59 of the Revision Guide to revise settings where services are provided, page 80 for hospice care, page 82 for domiciliary care, page 100 for later adulthood care, and page 108 for help with answering 'explain' questions.

Guided

(d) Discuss the responsibilities of healthcare workers when supporting people like Hal who have a terminal illness.

8 marks

The sample answer below states a responsibility in the first sentence and how this is achieved in the second sentence. There is a clear **link** between the two sentences – the **second** sentence **develops** the **first**. Linking and developing your answers is a quality that you need to show in answers to 'discuss' questions.

Marie Curie nurses are trained to provide high standards of care for people in their own homes. They are expected to maintain a professional approach, underpinned by the qualifications which they must have to become specialist nurses.

....

....

....

....

....

....

Continue the answer to explain a second responsibility of a healthcare worker. Note that the question does **not** ask you to write about a Marie Curie nurse, but you may if you wish to.

Go on to show that you know about other aspects of the roles of people who work in health and social care settings. The first sentence below is clearly **about care values**. The second sentence **explains how care values can be implemented**. Continue the answer to explain this point, with reference to multidisciplinary support. Go on to consider some benefits of being cared for at home or in a hospice.

One further aspect of palliative care is to support patients to live as actively as possible until they

die. Other healthcare staff might be involved to help the patient with psychological, social and

spiritual support. ....

....

....

....

....

Complete the conclusion below, stating the key care values that are relevant to the scenario, such as supporting the people who are close to the patient, managing pain and other symptoms (which is paramount in palliative care), affirming life and regarding dying as a normal process.

Finally, healthcare workers also have responsibilities to ....

....

....

....

....

To write a strong answer:
- demonstrate **accurate** and **thorough knowledge** of the responsibilities of healthcare workers when supporting people like Hal who have a terminal illness
- produce a **well-developed** and **balanced** discussion, including the benefits of home or hospice care
- show **clear**, **logical reasoning**, using specialist technical language

A good conclusion can strengthen your answer. For example, refer back to the key points of the question and briefly sum up your points.

Links Question 4(d) focuses on working with people with specific needs. Look at page 80 of the Revision Guide to revise hospice care, page 100 for caring for older adults, and page 109 for help with answering 'discuss' questions.

Total for Question 4 = 20 marks

END OF PAPER
TOTAL FOR PAPER = 80 MARKS

Revision paper 2

SECTION A

Answer ALL questions. Write your answers in the spaces provided.

1   **Scenario 1: Ill health**

Marquette is 34 weeks pregnant. She has regular appointments with her midwife, Gregory. He has monitored her health and that of her unborn child.

Marquette's preference is to have her baby in the birthing centre at her local maternity unit. She feels that she would have more support there if anything went wrong.

At 12 and 20 weeks Marquette had ultrasound scans and no problems were identified with the development of her baby. She decided that she preferred not to know the sex of her baby. Gregory is monitoring Marquette as she may be developing symptoms of pre-eclampsia and there is a family history of the condition.

Marquette starts to notice her womb tightening and is reassured by Gregory that this is normal at this stage of her pregnancy. He also confirms that possible symptoms of pre-eclampsia are no longer evident. At 36 weeks, contractions begin and she goes to the maternity unit where her baby is born.

Despite being born prematurely, Zowie is a healthy boy who weighs 4 kg.

Marquette returns home after two days in the maternity unit.

(a)   Apart from a midwife, identify **two** healthcare workers who might be present at the birth of Marquette's baby.

2 marks

1   ....

2   ....

(b)   Apart from giving ultrasound scans, describe **two** ways that healthcare workers might support Marquette during her pregnancy.

4 marks

Question 1(b) asks you to describe ways that **healthcare workers** give support **during** pregnancy. Consider the following ways of answering the questions:
- You can refer to **any healthcare worker** who helps Marquette during her pregnancy.
- You can include her **midwife** if you want to.
- If you wish, you can refer to **two different** healthcare workers for each way that you write about.

1   ....

....

....

....

2   ....

....

....

....

(c) Explain the role of a midwife in supporting a woman like Marquette when she has had her baby.

6 marks

Question 1(c) focuses on what happens **after** the baby is born and the role of a **midwife** during this time. You **must** write about what the **midwife** does. Make sure that you know how a midwife provides support through pregnancy, childbirth and during the first 28 days of a baby's life.

....

....

....

....

....

....

....

....

....

....

(d) Discuss ways that healthcare workers are accountable to professional bodies.

8 marks

To write a strong answer to Question 1(d), you need to:
- demonstrate **accurate** and **thorough knowledge** of the professional bodies that regulate healthcare workers such as midwives, nurses or doctors
- produce a **well-developed** and **balanced** discussion, showing an understanding of why healthcare workers are accountable, and of the needs of service users. You could refer to key care values to support the points you make
- show **clear**, **logical reasoning**, using specialist technical language.

A good conclusion can strengthen your answer. For example, refer back to the key points of the question and briefly sum up your points.

....

....

....

....

....

....

....

....

....

....

....

....

....

....

....

....

....

....

....

Links To help you answer the questions above, look at page 56 and 60 of the Revision Guide to revise the role and responsibilities of midwives, pages 71 and 91 to revise accountability to professional bodies, and pages 69, 70 and 72 to revise some key regulations which set out ways in which healthcare workers are accountable.

Total for Question 1 = 20 marks

SECTION B

Answer ALL questions. Write your answers in the spaces provided.

2 | **Scenario 2: Learning disability**

Imran is dyslexic, a condition which causes him to have problems with reading, writing and spelling. He also has dyspraxia, a condition which affects his physical coordination. With support from health visitors and medication prescribed by his GP, Imran has managed to control the symptoms of his dyspraxia and it now only affects him sometimes.

When he was at school, Imran would become frustrated that he could not complete tasks in the time he was given. This led to some disruptive behaviour. Other students in his class sometimes asked him and their teachers about the problems he had.

Since leaving school, Imran has had a successful career as a model. The model agencies which employ him know about his disability. They have provided some anti-discrimination training for other models and staff.

(a)   Identify **two** needs or rights that someone like Imran (who has learning disabilities) might have when attending school or college.

2 marks

> For Question 2(a) you can give two needs **or** two rights, **or** one of each.

1 ....

2 ....

(b)   Describe **two** ways that anti-discrimination training helps to prevent discrimination towards people with learning disabilities.

4 marks

> **Read the questions carefully**. For example, focus your responses to Question 2(b) on anti-discrimination training. The scenario tells you that the model agency provides anti-discrimination training but the model agency is not the focus of this question. So don't write about the model agency! Write only about anti-discrimination training in general.

1 ....

....

....

....

2 ....

....

....

....

(c) Explain the responsibilities of organisations which provide health and social care services towards the people they employ.

6 marks

Read the **questions carefully**. For example, Question 2(c) is about the responsibilities of health and social care organisations towards the **people they employ to work for** them. **Don't** write about people **who use** services. Include an example of a way that employees are protected.

....

....

....

....

....

....

....

....

....

....

(d) Discuss ways that confidentiality about people such as Imran is maintained by people who work in health and social care settings.

8 marks

To write a strong answer to Question 2(d), you need to:
- demonstrate **accurate** and **thorough knowledge** of ways that confidentiality is maintained by people who work in health and social care settings
- produce a **well-developed** and **balanced** discussion. You can refer to specific roles such as teachers, doctors or nurses. You may refer to Imran if you wish, but the question does not require this as it focuses on 'people such as Imran'. Include explanations and refer to key care values to support the points you make
- show **clear**, **logical reasoning**, using specialist technical language.

A good conclusion can strengthen your answer. For example, refer back to the key points of the question and briefly sum up your points.

....
....
....
....
....
....
....
....
....
....
....
....
....
....
....
....
....
....

Links To help you answer the questions above, look at pages 63–64 of the Revision Guide to revise anti-discriminatory practice, pages 65–66 for empowerment, pages 69–70 for data protection and ensuring confidentiality, page 72 for safeguarding regulations, pages 92–94 for standards, training and safeguarding employees, page 101 for policies, procedures and regulations, and page 97 for the care of people with learning disabilities.

Total for Question 2 = 20 marks

SECTION C

Answer ALL questions. Write your answers in the spaces provided.

3 | **Scenario 3: Physical / sensory disabilities**

Fay is 40 and she has been diagnosed with multiple sclerosis.

She has two young daughters. When they were first told about Fay's diagnosis, they were very upset. Recently, however, they have been helping Fay with some of her day-to-day routines.

Multiple sclerosis has a range of symptoms. These include extreme tiredness (fatigue), numbness and tingling, not being able to see clearly, problems with mobility and balance, and muscle weakness.

Fay is finding the Multiple Sclerosis Society a great support. It has given her information about symptoms, how she can manage her condition and how her family can support her.

Fay's home will be adapted and, in time, she will need respite care.

Following her care assessment, Fay will have a support worker for five afternoons a week.

(a) Identify **two** types of sensory disability which might affect Fay.

`2 marks`

Read the scenario carefully. For example, when answering Question 3(a), some types of sensory disability are referred to in the scenario. If you know others, you could decide which two to choose.

1 ....

2 ....

(b) Describe **two** ways that voluntary organisations, such as the Multiple Sclerosis Society, support people with specific needs.

`4 marks`

Read the question carefully. Question 3(b) refers to voluntary organisations **such as** the Multiple Sclerosis Society, so you **do not** have to refer to the Multiple Sclerosis Society – it is just an example of a voluntary organisation (charity). If you wish, you **may refer to any other** voluntary organisation that you know about. You may refer to **any** type of **specific need** – you **do not have to** write about multiple sclerosis.

1 ....

....

....

....

2 ....

....

....

....

(c)   Explain how care workers ensure safety when providing care and support for clients such as Fay.

6 marks

Read the question carefully. When answering Question 3(c) you may refer to **any** type of care worker – healthcare, personal care or both if you prefer. This question is about the responsibilities of care workers to ensure safety in care, so you need to say what they do in their day-to-day routines. You may refer to a specific health or personal care setting if you want to.

....

....

....

....

....

....

....

....

....

....

(d) Apart from ensuring safety, discuss the care priorities which occur when supporting someone like Fay who has physical and sensory disabilities.

8 marks

To write a strong answer to Question 3(d), you need to:

- demonstrate **accurate** and **thorough knowledge** of **care priorities** for **an individual like Fay** who has **specific needs**
- produce a **well-developed** and **balanced** discussion. Notice that the question starts with 'Apart from ensuring safety', so **don't** include points about ensuring safety in your answer or repeat points you made in answer to Question 3(c). To achieve balance in your discussion you might cover potentially conflicting care priorities such as the need to promote Fay's independence and her children's desire to be supported to help her. Refer to key care values to support the points you make
- show **clear**, **logical reasoning**, using specialist technical language.

A good conclusion can strengthen your answer. For example, refer back to the key points of the question and briefly sum up your points.

....
....
....
....
....
....
....
....
....
....
....
....
....
....
....
....
....
....

Links To help you answer the questions above, refer to pages 56, 58, 60 and 61 of the Revision Guide for roles and responsibilities of different workers, page 62 for supporting daily routines, page 67 for ensuring safety in care, page 68 for reports and complaints procedures, page 72 for safeguarding regulations, page 78 for the care provided by voluntary organisations, pages 83–84 for access to services, page 85 for representing service-user interests, and page 98 for caring for someone with a physical or sensory disability.

Total for Question 3 = 20 marks

SECTION D

Answer ALL questions. Write your answers in the spaces provided.

4 | **Scenario 4: Age-related needs**

Drake is 80. He was diagnosed with Alzheimer's, a type of dementia, when he was 75 and he is now at a late stage of the disease. He has an appointment every six months with his gerontologist, a doctor who specialises in illnesses in older people.

Because he is becoming increasingly weak, Drake is almost totally dependent on other people for care. He is currently living in a nursing home.

He has very little memory and is usually unable to recognise familiar objects or surroundings. From time to time, he does recognise people he knows, but usually he does not know who they are. This upsets members of his family.

Drake does not understand what is happening to him. At times he becomes very angry, especially when he is receiving personal care.

Drake may live for up to another five years but this depends on how his dementia develops.

(a) Apart from the gerontologist, identify **two** healthcare workers who might support Drake.

2 marks

> Question 1(a) starts with '**Apart** from the gerontologist…'. You don't need to know about the gerontologist to answer this question, and should not include a gerontologist in your answer.

1 ....

2 ....

(b) Describe **two** ways that members of Drake's family might support his needs and preferences.

4 marks

> Question 4(b) asks about how **members of Drake's family** support him, whereas Question 4(a) asks about **healthcare workers** who support him. You will draw on your knowledge and you might also draw on your own experience if you have provided care for someone you know.

1 ....

....

....

....

2 ....

....

....

....

(c) Explain ways that health and social care workers might support young children in Drake's family to cope with his dementia.

> For Question 4(c) you need to think about the ways that children react to bad news and the ways that they might need support. You may refer to their **needs and preferences** if you wish. The focus of the question is on supporting children to cope, rather than focusing on the dementia.

....

....

....

....

....

....

....

....

....

....

(d) Discuss issues which affect the ways that care is provided for people like Drake who cannot make their own decisions.

8 marks

> To write a strong answer, you need to:
> * demonstrate **accurate** and **thorough knowledge** about issues which affect the ways care is provided for people who cannot make their own decisions. This question is about advocacy and you should say what this means in your answer. You should say why Drake needs advocacy.
> * produce a **well-developed** and **balanced** discussion. Refer to key care values to support the points you make. Legislation protects people who are unable to make decisions for themselves. If you know about this, you could include it in your answer.
> * show **clear**, **logical reasoning**, using specialist technical language.
>
> A good conclusion can strengthen your answer. For example, refer back to the key points of the question and briefly sum up your points.

....

....

....

....

....

....

....

....

....

....

....

....

....

....

....

....

....

....

Links To help you answer the questions above, look at pages 56–61 of the Revision Guide to revise roles and responsibilities of health and social care workers, pages 65–66 for empowerment, page 73 for working in partnership, page 81 for residential care, pages 85–86 for representing service-user interests and advocacy, page 96 for mental ill health and page 100 for later adulthood care.

Total for Question 4 = 20 marks

END OF PAPER **TOTAL FOR PAPER = 80 MARKS**

Unit 3: Anatomy and Physiology for Health and Social Care

Your exam

You will have **1 hour 30 minutes** to complete your Unit 3 exam paper. You need to answer **every question** in the spaces provided. The paper is worth **90 marks** in total. The number of marks available for each question indicates the amount of time you should spend on that question. When in your exam:

- use **correct spelling, punctuation and grammar**
- use a pen that writes in **black** ink and make sure you also have a spare pen with you.

Your exam questions

Your exam will consist of groups of questions that focus on three areas.

The structure and organisation of the human body

For example, questions on some of the following:

- how cells work
- characteristics of tissues
- the structure and function of body organs
- energy in the body
- human genetics

The structure, function and disorders of body systems

For example, questions on some of the following:

- homeostatic mechanisms
- cardiovascular system
- respiratory system
- skeletal system
- muscular system
- digestive system
- nervous system
- endocrine system
- lymphatic and immune systems
- renal system
- reproductive system

Medical research

How data is collected and used.

You will be asked the following types of questions on which there is guidance in this workbook:

Complete	Define	Describe	In which	Provide a key
State	What	Which	Identify	Compare and contrast
Explain	Outline	By how many	To what extent	Deduce

> **Links** To help you revise for your Unit 3 exam this Workbook contains two full revision papers starting on pages 56 and 77. See the introduction on page iii for more information on features included to help you revise.

Revision paper 1

Answer ALL questions. Write your answers in the spaces provided.

Questions 1–3 are about the lungs.

1 The diagram shows a section through the lungs.

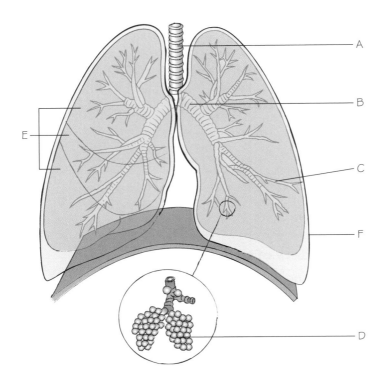

(a) Which letter points to the bronchioles?

....

 (b) State the names of structures **B**, **D** and **F**.

3 marks

'**State**' questions require you to **express facts** about something definitely or clearly.

B ....

D Alveoli

F ....

(c) These are descriptions of parts of the lungs.

A Encased in elastic fibres

B Repeatedly divides

C A group of globe-shaped structures

D Surrounded by capillaries

'Which' questions require you to pick an answer from a list. To answer it, you only need to write the letter that identifies your choice. If you are not sure about the answer, start by eliminating the ones you know are incorrect and then decide between the answers you have left. Never leave an answer blank. In this question, three of the statements describe the alveoli and one describes a bronchus.

Which statement describes a bronchus?

1 mark

....

 Links You can revise the respiratory system on pages 127–128 of the Revision Guide.

Total for Question 1 = 5 marks

2 | In a condition called cystic fibrosis, the glands lining the bronchi produce very thick mucus that is difficult to cough up. This leads to breathing difficulties.

Guided (a) Explain how cystic fibrosis leads to respiratory problems.

4 marks

- In 'Explain' questions you must show that you **understand** the origins, functions and objectives of a subject and its suitability for purpose. You should give **reasons to support** an opinion, view or argument, with clear details.
- You may find it useful to use words like 'therefore' and 'because', as these help to lead into and link your explanations.
- The first sentence of the answer has been done for you. Finish the next sentence by explaining the likely effects of the mucus on the lungs.

The mucus is very thick, so is difficult to cough up. This means that the lungs become clogged with

mucus. Therefore, ...

....

....

Now complete this question below, and go on to explain what is likely to happen to the lungs.

Over the years, the lungs become ....

....

....

....

Guided (b) Cystic fibrosis is a genetic disorder. Define the term *genetic disorder*.

1 mark

'**Define**' questions require you to give the definition of a word or term. This is similar to a 'State' question because it expects you to state the meaning of something.

The term 'genetic disorder' means ....

....

Links You can revise genetic disorders on page 120 of the Revision Guide.

Total for Question 2 = 5 marks

3 | The graph shows changes in the volume of air in the lungs during a routine check at a GP clinic.

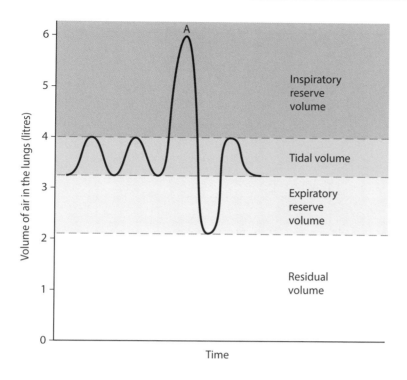

Guided

(a) Explain what the person has been asked to do at point A of the graph and the effect this will have on the composition of the air in their lungs.
2 marks

In 'Explain' questions you must show that you **understand** the topic and give **reasons to support** your answer. To answer this question, you need to write one sentence that says what the person has been asked to do at point A and how you know this.

You need to write a second sentence to explain the effect this will have on the composition of the air in the lungs.

The volume of air in the person's lungs has increased, so the person must have been asked to take

a deep breath. This means that the air in the lungs at point A ....

....

....

(b) State the names of the two volumes which, when added together, give the maximum volume of air the person can breathe in.
2 marks

In 'State' questions you only need to clearly express facts, which can be as little as one word. In this case, you need to pick the correct volumes from those used on the graph and write down their names.

A ....

B ....

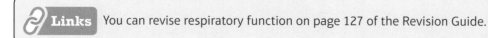 You can revise respiratory function on page 127 of the Revision Guide.

Total for Question 3 = 4 marks

Questions 4–6 are about the digestive system.

4 | The diagram shows the human digestive system.

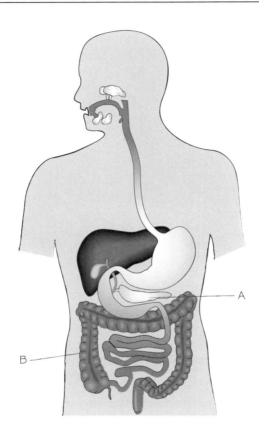

State the name of structures **A** and **B**.

2 marks

A Pancreas

B ....

> Links You can revise the digestive system on page 135 of the Revision Guide.

Total for Question 4 = 2 marks

5 The diagram shows a goblet cell and surrounding cells from the lining of the villi in the ileum.

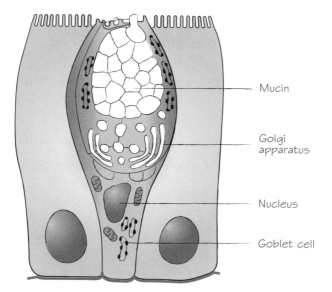

Mucin

Golgi apparatus

Nucleus

Goblet cell

A Cubiodal
B Columnar
C Squamous
D Ciliated

(a) To which type of tissue do the cells in the diagram belong?

1 mark

'**To which**' questions require you to specify a particular item. Here, you only need to write letter A, B, C or D, to indicate which type of cell you think is the right answer.

....

> **Guided**

(b) Outline why both simple and compound epithelial cells are found in the digestive system.

3 marks

In '**Outline**' questions you need to provide a **summary, overview** or a **brief description** of something. To make your answer clear, you can use a separate sentence to outline each of the main points you wish to cover. The first sentence on the first point has been written for you. You now need to complete a similar sentence about compound epithelial cells which shows that you know where these are found in the digestive system and why they are needed.

Simple epithelial cells are found in areas which are not subject to abrasion, such as the villi, and

where secretion of mucus is needed to trap unwanted particles and act as a lubricant to move them

on. Compound epithelial cells are found in areas which are ....

....

....

⊘ Links You can revise epithelial tissues on page 114 of the Revision Guide.

Total for Question 5 = 4 marks

6 Peptic ulcers are a common disorder of the digestive system. The symptoms of peptic ulcers are stomach pain, vomiting, bloating and heartburn.

Guided (a) Explain what happens in the stomach to cause these symptoms. 2 marks

In 'Explain' questions, you need to demonstrate your **understanding** by giving **reasons to support** what you say. To make your answer clear, you can use a separate sentence to explain each of the main points you wish to cover. The first sentence has been written for you. You now need to write a second sentence to explain what happens now there is an open sore.

Gastric juices and stomach acid in the stomach destroy a small area of mucous membrane, producing

an open sore. ....

....

....

Guided (b) A study was done on the probability of developing ulcer complications when taking various forms of medication. The results are shown in the bar chart.

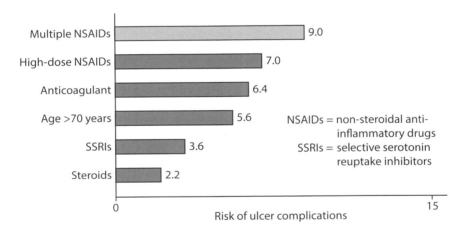

NSAIDs = non-steroidal anti-inflammatory drugs
SSRIs = selective serotonin reuptake inhibitors

By how many times was the probability of developing ulcer complications greater for patients who take high-dose NSAIDs compared with those who take steroids? 2 marks

In '**By how many**' questions, you need to calculate an item in relation to another. In this question, you need to look at the bar chart to find out the probability of each of the two types of patients developing ulcer complications and divide the higher number by the lower number. You know from both the question and the bar chart that the probability is **greater** so your answer will be a number higher than 1. You can express your answer either as the number of times it has increased, or convert it to a percentage by multiplying the answer by 100. If expressing the answer as a percentage increase, you must use the % sign.

Answer 7.0 ÷ 2.2 = ...

Guided

(c)   To what extent do these data support the conclusion that high-dose NSAIDs cause ulcers?

3 marks

In 'To what extent questions' you must include **clear details** and give clear **reasons and/or evidence to support** an opinion, view or argument. You could show how you arrived at your conclusion. The first sentence has been written for you. You now need to write a sentence stating any ways in which the data may not support this conclusion, followed by a third sentence in which you give your own conclusion.

The bar chart shows that there is a correlation between the use of some prescription drugs and an

increased probability of developing ulcer complications. However, ...

....

....

....

....

Links   You can revise disorders of the digestive system on page 138 of the Revision Guide.

Total for Question 6 = 7 marks

Question 7 is about energy and homeostasis.

7 (a) State the *law of conservation of energy*. `1 mark`

....

....

(b) One way in which the body controls an increasing temperature is by sweating. This is part of the process of homeostasis. The flow diagram shows this process.

Stimulus Body temperature _____

Sun, fire, etc. Hot food or drink. Infection

Receptors Thermal receptors in _____ and around _____

Nerve impulses

Control centre Temperature control centre in brain switches on heat-losing mechanisms

Effectors Nerve impulses

_____ activated:
• sweat poured onto skin surface
• evaporation of water removes heat energy from skin – cooling occurs

_____ dilated:
• increased blood flow to skin
• skin warm and pink
• radiation of heat from surface – cooling

Behaviour altered by:
_____
_____
_____
_____
_____
_____
_____

NB Other methods of heat loss from the skin (i.e. conduction and convection) still occur, but cannot be increased to any significant level

Response Body temperature _____

State the body parts involved as effectors by completing the gaps on the diagram. `2 marks`

(c) Identify how the system would react if the body's temperature increased by completing the diagram. One has been done for you. `4 marks`

'State' and 'Identify' questions require you to recall **knowledge** and give a **fact** or indicate the main features or purposes of something, to show you understand the facts or qualities. In this question, you are required to recall the facts about how thermal receptors in the skin and around internal organs are stimulated by the hypothalamus and what happens next to decrease the body's temperature. Part of each box has been completed to guide you through this question.

Links You can revise the law of conservation of energy on page 117 of the Revision Guide and control of body temperature on page 121.

Total for Question 7 = 7 marks

Questions 8–11 are about the skeletal system.

8 Increasing age increases the likelihood of broken bones. The bar chart shows the number of fractures suffered by people of various age groups in the UK during one year.

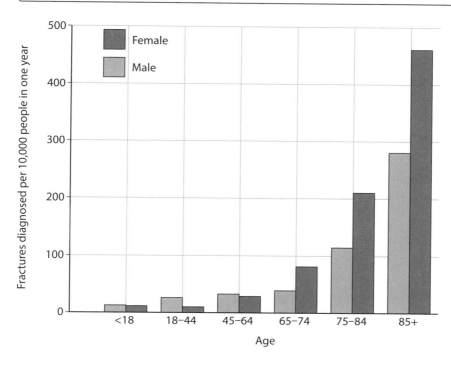

Guided (a) Explain the change in the bones of both genders with increasing age.　　**4 marks**

> This question asks you to **explain** changes in bones of both genders for the different age ranges shown on the bar chart. For each of the age groups given below in the answer, you need to provide the relevant explanation. Complete the explanation in the first age range, then complete the final sentence about disorders which older people tend to develop, explaining why these lead to more broken bones.

Up to age group '45 to 64'

As babies and children develop and grow, their bones become harder and are more likely to break

when they fall. As they become young people and adults, they take up more ....

....

and start working, so are more likely to break bones.

From age group '45 to 64' onwards

As people age, their bones become less dense and more brittle, so that even a minor accident can

lead to a break. They are also more likely to develop disorders such as ....

....

....

....

(b) State the name of the vitamin which children who don't play outdoors may lack, so causing their bones to be softer and more likely to break.　　**1 mark**

....

Guided ▷

(c) Describe the event that occurs as females age, which results in a reversal of the trend of males sustaining more breaks than females.

4 marks

> In 'Describe' questions you must give a **clear, objective account** in your own words, showing recall and, in some cases, application of the relevant **features and information** about a subject. Make sure you read the question carefully and only use information that answers the question. You will not be given marks for additional, irrelevant information.
>
> The answer to this question is worth 4 marks so you need to write at least four sentences. Each sentence has been started for you. Ensure the last one sums up the reason for the reverse in the trend.

The menopause is when ....

....

Women usually go through the menopause between ....

....

Osteoporosis in women is often associated with ....

....

This is why the reverse in the trend only starts to appear ....

....

Total for Question 8 = 9 marks

9 The skeleton is divided into two parts called the axial skeleton and the appendicular skeleton.

(a) In which part of the skeleton is the skull?

1 mark

....

'In which' questions require you to specify a particular item. Do not assume that, because you have a choice of two parts of the skeleton and there are two questions, the answer to (b) will be different from (a). They may be the same.

(b) In which part of the skeleton is the spine?

1 mark

....

Total for Question 9 = 2 marks

10 One of the key actions of joints is flexion.

> Guided

Define the term *flexion*.

1 mark

'Flexion' describes the action when the ....

....

Total for Question 10 = 1 mark

11 | Cartilage and ligaments are important parts of the skeletal system and can both be found in joints.

> Guided >

(a) Compare and contrast cartilage and ligaments.

[3 marks]

In **'Compare and contrast'** questions you identify the main factors relating to two or more items, situations or aspects of a subject and explain the similarities, differences, advantages and disadvantages. It is important that you make **links.** Complete the sentences to give key facts such as structure, function and flexibility, then sum up the similarities and differences.

Cartilage is the smooth, translucent, cushioning substance that ....

....

....

Ligaments are strap-like strong elasticated bands that run from ....

....

....

Although both are ....

....

> Guided >

(b) A carer working in a residential care home helps to lift service users on a daily basis, often using a hoist. Explain the possible damage caused to the carer's skeletal system of not using a hoist when lifting a person who is morbidly obese and who has limited mobility.

[4 marks]

Make sure you answer the question asked and do not write about the wrong body system. In this question you are asked about the **skeletal** system, so do not write about muscle strain, which relates to the muscular system, or problems such as carpal tunnel syndrome, which affects the nervous system.

It is important for the carer to be aware of the range of movements allowed by different types of

joint ....

....

There is a risk of overstretching, straining or even snapping tendons and ligaments when ....

....

There is the possibility of irritating joints and discs, which ....

....

Doing the same motion over and over again ....

....

 Links You can revise the skeletal system, joints and disorders on pages 130–132 of the Revision Guide.

Total for Question 11 = 7 marks

Questions 12–13 are about the lymphatic and immune systems.

12 The diagram shows the lymphatic system of a human.

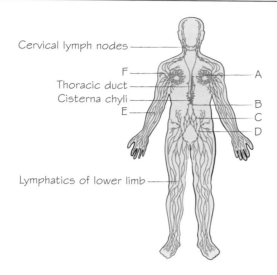

Guided (a) State the letters that label the axillary lymph nodes and the lymphatics of the mammary gland.

2 marks

Axillary lymph nodes ....

Lymphatics of the mammary gland ....

Guided (b) A healthy person's lymphatic system includes five lymphatic organs, each of which performs one of the following five functions:

> **A** Traps pathogens and produces antibodies
> **B** Contains lymphatic vessels that regulate pathogens
> **C** Filters blood and releases lymphocytes in response to pathogens
> **D** Site for maturation, development and control of lymphocytes
> **E** Filters micro-organisms, such as bacteria, and cancer cells

Complete the table with the relevant letter for each organ.

5 marks

To answer questions like this, first fill in the letters for the answers you are confident about. Then use your knowledge of the subject to try to work out the correct answers for the letters you have left, and complete the table. You should never leave a space blank.

Organ	Function (A, B, C, D or E)
Lymph nodes	
Thymus	
Spleen	
Tonsils	
Appendix	B

(c) Which organ is also part of the endocrine system?

1 mark

....

Total for Question 12 = 8 marks

13 | Hodgkin's disease, also called Hodgkin's lymphoma, is an uncommon cancer of the lymphatic and immune systems. This condition causes usually painless swellings in the neck, armpit or groin, and – in some patients – a high temperature.

Guided

(a) Explain why Hodgkin's disease causes swellings and a high temperature.   `4 marks`

> The answer below starts with a sentence that explains what is in the swelling, followed by another sentence about the effect of this excess. Having explained what causes the swellings, another two sentences explain why some patients develop a temperature. Complete the sentences so that you make four different points.

The swelling is caused by an excess of ....

....

These ....

....

This causes the lymphocytes to lose ....

....

....

> Another disorder of the lymphatic and immune systems is leukaemia, which is cancer of the white blood cells.

Guided

(b) Explain why doctors classify leukaemia as a disorder of the lymphatic and immune systems, when blood is considered to be part of the cardiovascular system.   `4 marks`

> This question requires you to show your knowledge and understanding of leukaemia. You need to show that you know what leukaemia is, that the various types are caused by abnormal white blood cells and how it affects people who have the condition. You need to finish your answer by drawing together the points which show why leukaemia is considered a disorder of the lymphatic and immune systems.

There are many types of leukaemia, which is ....

....

The two main types affect ....

....

People with leukaemia have repeated ....

....

Leukaemia therefore mainly affects ....

....

> **Links** You can revise the lymphatic and immune systems and disorders of these systems on pages 143–144 of the Revision Guide.

Total for Question 13 = 8 marks

Questions 14–16 are about the female and male reproductive systems.

14 During the fertility cycle, ovulation occurs due to various changes in hormone levels. Increasing levels of oestrogen trigger an increase in a hormone called LH which in turn causes the release of the mature egg from the ovary. The diagram shows a woman's fertility cycle.

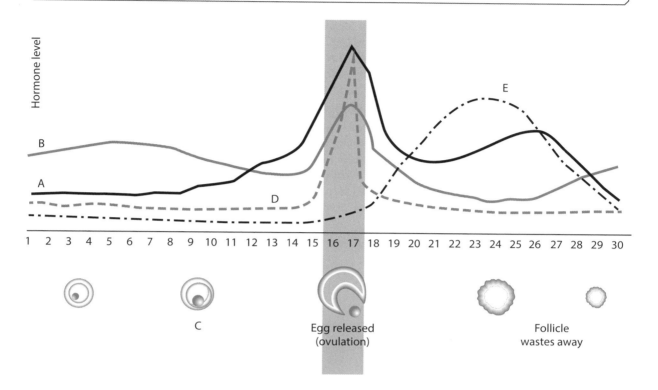

State the letters that label the oestrogen level and the LH level.

2 marks

Oestrogen ....

LH ....

Always **read the information at the start of questions carefully**. In this question the oestrogen and LH levels can only be A or D, because these are the ones which continue to increase before the egg is released. B increases but decreases again, so B can be eliminated as a possible answer. From the information decide which increases first, the oestrogen or the LH. The one which increases first is the oestrogen and second the LH.

Total for Question 14 = 2 marks

71

15 Endometrial cells are usually found in the lining of the uterus. Endometriosis is a disorder of the female reproductive system, in which patches of endometrial cells are found elsewhere in the body but are under the same hormonal influences as those in the uterus, so go through the same process of building up, breaking down and bleeding. The blood and debris from these patches has nowhere to go, which leads to symptoms such as pain and infertility.

One study of 138 girls who had their condition diagnosed before the age of 21 showed that most had other medical conditions. In 58% of these cases they had conditions which generated pain, such as irritable bowel syndrome (IBS), chronic headaches and lower back pain, and these girls were significantly more likely to suffer from depression and anxiety. 57 out of 138 girls had tried at least three different hormone treatments for endometriosis, suggesting that there is much trial and error when it comes to treating this condition.

Studies of the disease show that symptoms are presented in adolescence and that early diagnosis can lessen the impact of the disease and reduce infertility. One method of diagnosing the condition is laparoscopy, a surgical procedure with the risks, costs and waiting lists associated with surgery. One study has been conducted in Germany to investigate whether magnetic resonance imaging (MRI), which is a non-invasive method, can be used accurately to find different types of endometriosis in the body. They identified 152 women who had suspected endometriosis, gave each an MRI scan, then a full laparoscopy investigation. They compared the results from both methods.

The data is shown below. The larger the percentage the more successful the accuracy of using the MRI method proved to be.

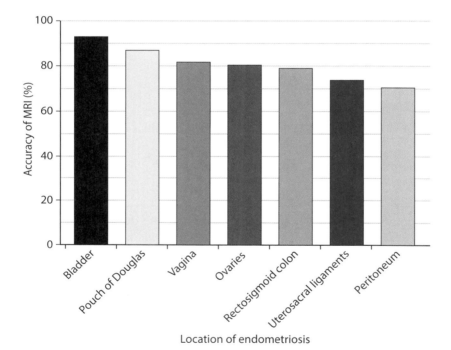

Location of endometriosis

Conclusions: The researchers of the first study concluded that the same additional painful conditions were more common in adult women with endometriosis than in younger women, suggesting that the longer women spend suffering with endometriosis the more detrimental the effect on the body as a whole.

The researchers of the second study concluded that, overall, MRI performs quite well, particularly in identifying endometriosis of the bladder and pouch of Douglas (the gap just behind the uterus).

Guided

To what extent does the data support these conclusions?

To what extent questions require you to look at facts and opinions, in whatever form they are given, and show your understanding of them. These questions are worth up to 8 marks. Complete the following answer, making at least eight different points. Make sure you include comments that support the facts, and give arguments against any opinions that you don't feel to be accurate. Finish your answer with a comment that sums up what you think overall.

Although the data from the first study shows that ....

....

....

We are not told how many ....

....

....

In the second study, MRI identified ....

....

However, it only ....

....

....

....

....

The conclusion that MRI detects endometriosis 'quite well' is, therefore, ...

....

....

Again, there is not ....

....

....

MRI is useful when it successfully detects endometriosis but ....

....

....

Overall, the studies provided ....

....

Links You can revise the female reproductive system on page 146, and disorders of the reproductive system on page 148 of the Revision Guide.

Total for Question 15 = 8 marks

16 Prostate cancer is a disorder of the male reproductive system. It is diagnosed and monitored by blood tests to determine the level of prostate-specific antigen (PSA) in the blood. Radiotherapy is one of the treatments for localised prostate cancer. This graph shows the proportion of patients free from a recurrence of prostate cancer in the years following various doses of radiotherapy.

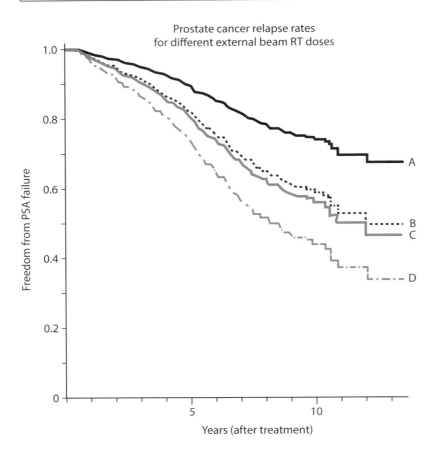

Prostate cancer relapse rates for different external beam RT doses

Freedom from PSA failure

Years (after treatment)

 Guided

(a) Using the information given in the graph and the key so far, provide a key for the graph. One has been done for you.

2 marks

In 'Provide a key' questions, you need to correspond one item to another. In this case, you need to match a dosage to the correct line on the graph, after reading all the information provided.

Dosage of 70–74.9 Gy: C

Dosage of 75–79.9 Gy: ....

Dosage of more than 80 Gy: ....

Dosage of less than 70 Gy: ....

(b) If an external beam radiation therapy (EBRT) cures the patient, the downward trend should level off and become a horizontal line.

What number of years after receiving a dosage of 70–74.9 Gy may patients start to hope they have been cured?

1 mark

In 'What' questions you pick an item from a list or read it from a table or graph.

Answer..

Links You can revise the male reproductive system and disorders on pages 147–148 of the Revision Guide.

Total for Question 16 = 3 marks

Question 17 is about human genetics.

17 | Studies of a family with a genetically inherited condition, sickle cell disease, revealed the family tree shown below.

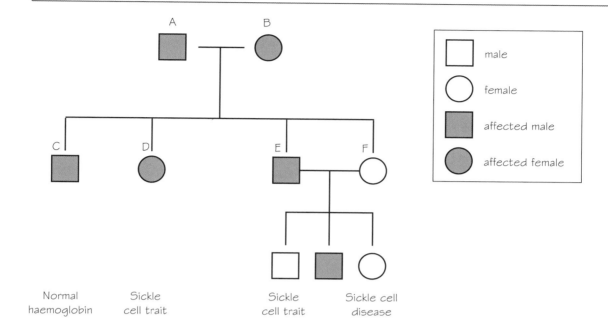

| | Normal haemoglobin | Sickle cell trait | | Sickle cell trait | Sickle cell disease |

🔗 **Links** You can revise inheritance and genetic diseases on pages 118–120 of the Revision Guide.

Guided

Deduce the probability of an individual with E's genotype being born to parents A and B. You must include a suitable genetic diagram in your answer.

8 marks

- In 'Deduce' questions you reach a conclusion about something by **reasoning**. Questions on genetics usually require you to deduce something from a family tree.
- In this question, you need to draw a genetics diagram to help you deduce the answer. Make sure that you correctly label the diagram. The diagram has been drawn for you and some of the gametes included to help you.
- You need to finish labelling the diagram and then deduce the correct answer, explaining your reasoning in coming to this answer.
- You will deduce that E's genotype will be Ss and you need to say how you know this.
- You then need to deduce that A and B are both Ss, and explain why.
- Finally, you must correctly deduce the ratio in which parents of genotype Ss can have children of the various genotypes.
- This will lead you to the answer of a probability of 50%, or one in two.

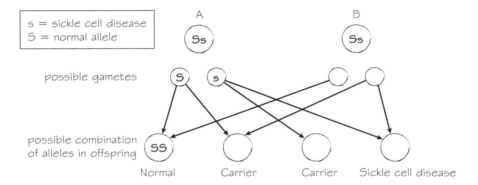

E's genotype is Ss because some of his children are unaffected and ....

Both parents A and B must be Ss, so have ....

....

The gene for sickle cell disease must be .... To have sickle cell

disease, a child must have ....

....

Parents A and B can have children of genotypes ....

....

in the ratio of 1:2:1 as shown ....

There is a one in two chance ....

....

....

Total for Question 17 = 8 marks

END OF PAPER
TOTAL FOR PAPER = 90 MARKS

Revision paper 2

Answer ALL questions. Write your answers in the spaces provided.

Questions 1–3 are about the skin.

1 The diagram shows a sensory neurone from the skin.

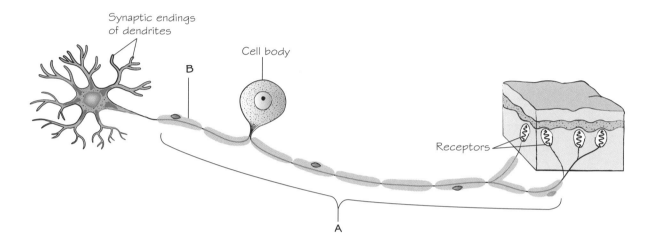

Synaptic endings of dendrites

B

Cell body

Receptors

A

State the name of structures **A** and **B**. **2 marks**

A ....

B ....

Links You can revise sensory neurones on page 139 of the Revision Guide.

Total for Question 1 = 2 marks

2 | The diagram shows some types of tissue from the skin. These are labelled **A** and **B**.

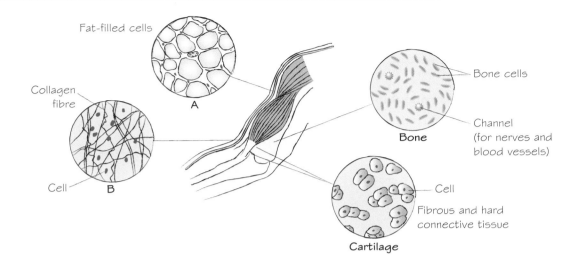

A Areolar
B Nervous
C Adipose
D Epithelial

(a) To which kind of tissue does the cell type labelled A belong?

1 mark

....

(b) Outline where and why both of cell types A and B are found in the skin.

3 marks

....
....
....
....
....

Links You can revise tissue types on pages 113–115 of the Revision Guide.

Total for Question 2 = 4 marks

3 Normal skin has sebaceous glands which produce oils to keep skin supple and waterproof. Eczema is a common disorder of the skin. The symptoms of eczema are patches of itchy, dry and cracked skin.

(a) Explain what happens in the skin to cause the symptoms of eczema.

2 marks

Question 3(a) is testing your understanding of the skin and the function of healthy skin. Think about what must happen in the skin to make it dry.

....

....

....

....

....

(b) A study was carried out to identify the percentage of children developing allergic conditions on different continents. The results are shown in the bar chart.

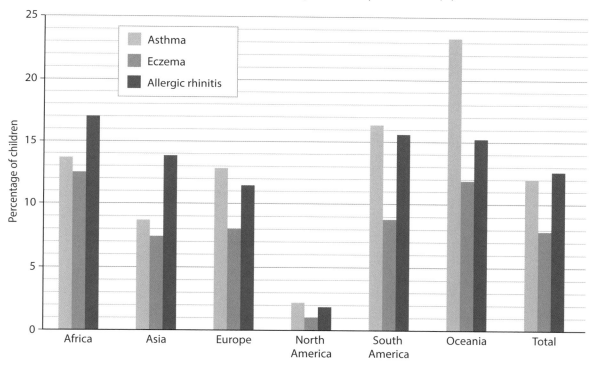

Prevalence (extent) of allergic disorders per continent (%)

By how many times was the probability of developing eczema greater for a child living in Europe than for a child living in North America?

2 marks

....

....

Use the key to find out which bars represent children with eczema. Read the values you need off the *y*-axis and compare the two, using division.

(c) To what extent do these data support the conclusion that children who develop eczema are likely to develop asthma and allergic rhinitis as well?

3 marks

You do not need detailed knowledge of these conditions in order to answer this question. You are being asked about **what the data tell you**. Remember, it is possible that the data you are given do not support the hypothesis you are being asked to consider. If so, do the data suggest a different hypothesis to you?

....

....

....

....

....

....

Links You can revise data analysis on pages 154–157 of the Revision Guide.

Total for Question 3 = 7 marks

Question 4 is about energy metabolism in the body.

4 │ Cellular respiration is a series of metabolic reactions which releases energy that is stored in chemicals. Aerobic respiration takes place in mitochondria, whereas anaerobic respiration takes place in the cytoplasm.

(a) Define *metabolism*.

1 mark

....

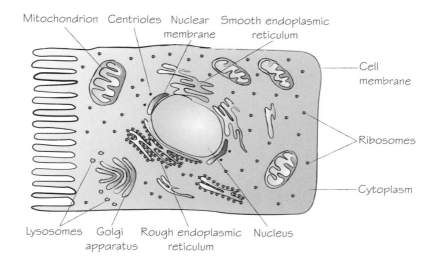

Mitochondrion Centrioles Nuclear Smooth endoplasmic
                           membrane   reticulum

Cell
membrane

Ribosomes

Cytoplasm

Lysosomes Golgi Rough endoplasmic Nucleus
           apparatus   reticulum

(b) Identify some differences between aerobic and anaerobic respiration by completing the table. One difference has been done for you.

5 marks

Aerobic respiration	Anaerobic respiration
Needs oxygen – yes or no?	Needs oxygen – yes or no? ....
Waste products: 1 .... 2	Waste product: ....
Large amount of energy from the breakdown of food	Small amount of energy from the breakdown of food

(c) State the primary type of respiration that takes place in the cells of an athlete running a 100 m race.

1 mark

....

Links You can revise metabolism on page 117 of the Revision Guide.

Total for Question 4 = 7 marks

Questions 5–7 are about the renal system.

5 The diagram shows the major organs in the body, including the kidneys.

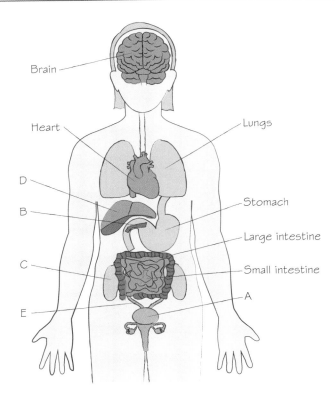

(a) Which letter points to the kidneys?   `1 mark`

....

(b) State the names of structures A, D and E.   `3 marks`

A ....

D ....

E ....

(c) These are descriptions of parts of the kidney:

> **A** Urine drains into this
> **B** Enters kidney after branching off from the abdominal aorta
> **C** Made up of seven cone-shaped structures
> **D** Joins with the inferior vena cava

Which statement describes the renal artery?   `1 mark`

....

 Links You can revise major organs on page 116 and the renal system on page 145 of the Revision Guide.

Total for Question 5 = 5 marks

6 In a condition called renal failure, the kidneys stop working properly. This leads to tiredness, blood in the urine, swollen ankles, feet or hands, nausea and shortness of breath.

(a) Explain how renal failure leads to swollen feet.

4 marks

> Think about the **role of the kidneys** in the body and what will happen if they stop performing their role effectively.

....

....

....

....

....

....

....

....

(b) Renal disease is progressive. Define the term *progressive*.

1 mark

....

....

Links You can revise disorders of the renal system on page 145 of the Revision Guide.

Total for Question 6 = 5 marks

7 The graph shows a strong correlation between kidney disease and diabetes. Diabetes is a disorder of blood sugar regulation, caused by a lack of or resistance to insulin, a hormone which is made in the pancreas.

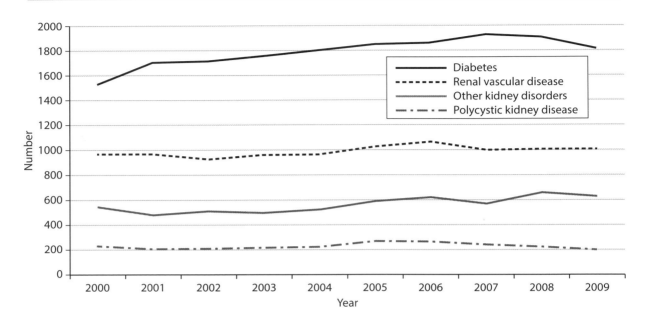

(a) The graph shows a strong correlation between the number of people suffering from diabetes and the number of people with various kidney disorders, suggesting that those with diabetes, which damages the small blood vessels in the body, are more at risk of suffering kidney failure than those without diabetes. Explain why this is likely to be true. 〔2 marks〕

Think about the **role of the kidneys** and what happens in that role when the blood vessels in the kidneys become damaged.

....

....

....

....

(b) Diabetes can also cause nerve damage, which can lead to difficulties emptying the bladder. State **two** ways in which this can damage the renal system. 〔2 marks〕

Think about (a) the **pressure** building up in the bladder and backing up in the renal system, (b) the effect of **bacteria** in urine that has a high sugar level.

1 ....

2 ....

 Links You can revise kidney function on page 145 and diabetes on pages 122 and 142 of the Revision Guide.

Total for Question 7 = 4 marks

Questions 8–9 are about the muscular system.

8   The diagram shows the muscular system of a human.

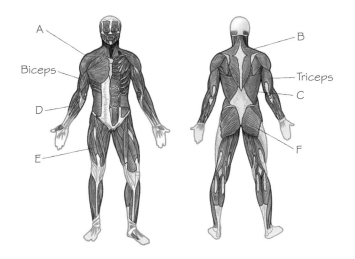

(a)   State the letters that label the deltoids and the gluteus.

2 marks

Deltoids ....

Gluteus ....

A Eccentric

B Shortens

C Isometric

D Lengthens

E Stays the same

F Concentric

(b)   Complete the table with the relevant letter for either the name of the type of contraction or the change in length of the contracting muscle.

6 marks

Type of contraction	Change in length of contracting muscle	Example of use	Resulting action
		Carrying an object in front of you at one level, e.g. at shoulder height, or gripping a tennis racket	No movement in bones or joint(s) but muscle keeps bone(s) steady
		Kicking a football	Control or deceleration of a movement
		Bending the elbow from a straight arm to fully flexed	General movement of bones

Links   You can revise the muscular system on pages 133–134 of the Revision Guide.

Total for Question 8 = 8 marks

9 Muscular dystrophy is a very rare genetic condition affecting just over 1 in 1000 people. It causes a gradual weakening of the muscles, which may eventually cease to function.

(a) Explain why muscular dystrophy causes muscles to weaken.

4 marks

....

....

....

....

....

....

....

....

Whereas muscular dystrophy is a condition of the muscular system caused by weakened muscles, rickets is a disorder of the skeletal system caused by weak or soft bones. Until the last ten years, rickets had become very rare in the UK, but since then there has been a four-fold rise in the occurrence of rickets in children.

(b) Explain why some doctors think that changes in children's lifestyles may be a cause of the increase in cases of rickets.

4 marks

Think about how **technology** has affected the leisure time of a lot of children and how parental attitudes to children **playing outside** in the sun and playing **unsupervised** seem to have changed.

....

....

....

....

....

....

....

Links You can revise disorders of the muscular system on page 133 of the Revision Guide and disorders of the skeletal system on page 132.

Total for Question 9 = 8 marks

Questions 10–13 are about the digestive system.

10 | Food and chyme move down the alimentary canal by a process known as peristalsis. The diagram shows how the muscles of the alimentary canal cause a peristaltic wave.

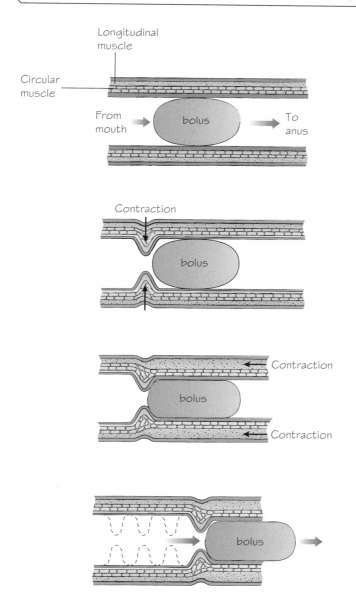

(a) Explain how the action of the pairs of muscles changes to apply pressure at two different stages to push the food along.

4 marks

Before the bolus ....

....

....

....

....

After the bolus ....

....

....

....

(b)   State the site within the pancreas where the hormones insulin and glucagon are made.   `1 mark`

....

(c)   Describe the processes that happen in the stomach during digestion.   `4 marks`

....

....

....

....

....

....

....

....

> **Links**   You can revise the digestive system on pages 135–138 of the Revision Guide. Revise the hormones produced by the pancreas on page 141.

Total for Question 10 = 9 marks

11   The breakdown and absorption of food is divided into stages called ingestion, digestion, absorption and egestion.

(a)   In which stage are simple soluble molecules passed into the bloodstream?   `1 mark`

....

(b)   In which stage does waste material pass out of the body?   `1 mark`

....

> **Links**   You can revise the stages of digestion on page 135 of the Revision Guide.

Total for Question 11 = 2 marks

12   A number of processes occur in the digestion system.

Define the term *deamination*.   `1 mark`

....

> **Links**   You can revise enzymes and products of digestion on page 136 of the Revision Guide.

Total for Question 12 = 1 mark

13 | Enzymes and micro-organisms are essential to the process of digesting food.

(a) Compare and contrast the roles of enzymes and micro-organisms in digestion.

`3 marks`

....

....

....

....

....

....

....

> Think about what enzymes and micro-organisms are and what they do in the body.

(b) A man has been tested by his doctor and diagnosed with hepatitis. Explain what he needs to know about the disorder before he can decide how to adapt his lifestyle to help improve his health.

`4 marks`

....

....

....

....

....

....

....

> You need to write about what hepatitis is, what causes it, the symptoms and how it can be treated.

Links You can revise the digestive system and its disorders on pages 135–138 of the Revision Guide.

Total for Question 13 = 7 marks

Questions 14–16 are about the male and female reproductive systems.

14 | The diagram shows the male reproductive system.

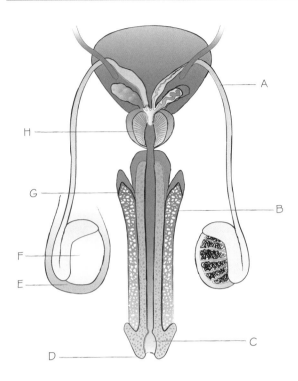

State the letters that label the urethra and the prostate gland.

2 marks

Urethra ....

Prostate gland ....

Links You can revise the male reproductive system on page 147 of the Revision Guide.

Total for Question 14 = 2 marks

15 Prostate cancer is a disorder of the male reproductive system and is the most common male cancer in England, accounting for 26% of all newly diagnosed cases of cancer among men in 2010.

A study was carried out to investigate how age is related to the survival rate and to compare the incidence of prostate cancer with the mortality rate. Prostate cancer was the second most common cause of cancer death in men in 2010, after lung cancer.

In the early 1990s, diagnosis improved due to increased use of prostate-specific antigen (PSA) testing in men aged over 50. The data collected showed that survival is slightly lower for men aged 15–49 years (90%) than for those aged 50–69 years (92%). Some of the data is shown in the graph below.

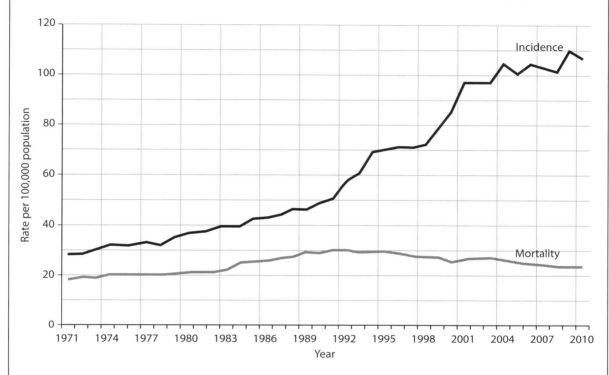

The researchers concluded that the increase in the incidence of prostate cancer in the early 1990s was due to improved diagnosis from increased use of prostate-specific antigen (PSA) testing.

To what extent does the data support this conclusion?

8 marks

Read the information given carefully and look closely at the graph to identify trends in incidence and mortality, and note what happened to both in the early 1990s.

....

....

....

....

....

....

....

....

....

....

....

....

....

....

....

....

....

....

....

....

....

....

Links You can revise the male reproductive system and its disorders on pages 147 and 148 of the Revision Guide.

Total for Question 15 = 8 marks

16 Doctors are able to plot information about a woman's menstrual cycle to identify when she is most likely to ovulate, to help her conceive.

Graph A shows the concentration of FSH and LH in plasma during a woman's menstrual cycle. Ovulation occurred on day 16 of her cycle. LH rises two days after oestrogen to reach a peak, resulting in ovulation.

Graph B shows the concentration of two hormones, oestrogen and progesterone, produced in the ovary during the same menstrual cycle. Oestrogen rises, inhibiting FSH, and reaches a peak just before ovulation. It then rapidly declines.

Graph A

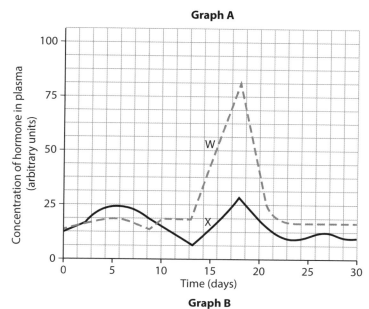

Graph B

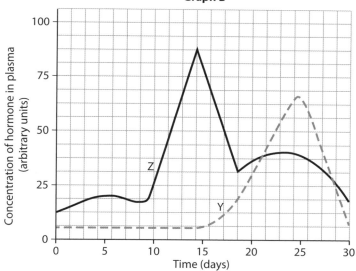

(a) Using all the information given, provide a key for the graph. One has been done for you.

2 marks

You don't need to have studied graphs of female hormones before in order to answer this question. To work out which line corresponds to which letter, you need to read the information about both graphs given in the introduction to the question

Progesterone ....

FSH: X ....

Oestrogen ....

LH ....

93

(b)   What is the concentration of FSH after ovulation at the point when oestrogen reaches a dip, before it rises again?

1 mark

Answer ....

🔗 **Links**   You can revise data analysis of graphs on page 156 of the Revision Guide.

Total for Question 16 = 3 marks

Question 17 is about human genetics.

17 | Studies of a family with a genetically inherited condition, cystic fibrosis, revealed the family tree shown below.

Questions on genetics usually require you to **deduce** something from a family tree. In this question, you need to draw a genetic diagram to help you deduce the answer. One mark is awarded for the correctly labelled diagram. You need to use the family tree and your genetic diagram to deduce the correct answer, **explaining your reasoning** in coming to this answer.

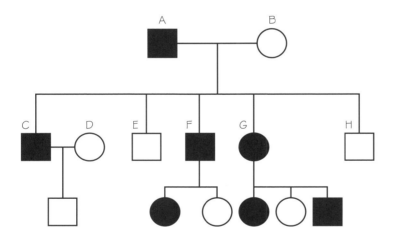

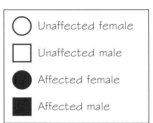

Deduce the probability of an individual with D's genotype being born to parents A and B. You must include a suitable genetic diagram in your answer.

8 marks

Links You can revise inheritance of genetic disorders on pages 118–120 of the Revision Guide.

Total for Question 17 = 8 marks

END OF PAPER   TOTAL FOR PAPER = 90 MARKS

Unit 4: Enquiries into Current Research in Health and Social Care

Your set task

Your Unit 4 set task requires you to use your understanding of research methodologies and associated issues related to a piece of current research on a health or social care issue, along with your own skills in carrying out secondary research around the issue. You then answer four questions based on the research.

Part A – Set task brief and research

You will be given Part A **six weeks before** your Part B assessment. You will have **18 hours** to:

- choose one of two provided articles covering an aspect of recent research, on which to analyse and to base your secondary research
- carry out your own independent secondary research using at least two secondary research sources related to the issue
- prepare a list of your secondary sources and notes on your secondary research – you can take up to six sides of A4 notes into your Part B supervised assessment.

Part B – Completing your set task

Your Part B supervised assessment is worth **65 marks**. You will be asked questions relating to the provided article and your own secondary research sources. You will have a total of **three hours over three days** and will be able to refer to your six sides of A4 notes from Part A. Suggestions for how you might allocate your time are noted in brackets below. You will be asked four questions that focus on:

1   understanding **research methods** and the **validity** and **reliability of results** in research (15 marks; 40 minutes)

2   understanding the **relationship** between **your own secondary research** and the **provided article**, and how this relationship reinforces the **importance of the issue** (15 marks; 40 minutes)

3   **planning** and **ethical** considerations for **further research** (15 marks; 40 minutes)

4   **research implications** for **future provision** and/or **practice** (20 marks; 50 minutes).

You will also list the secondary sources you have used (10 minutes).

At the end of the assessment you will submit your completed taskbook. Your prepared notes do not need to be submitted.

Your Workbook

This Workbook helps you to revise your skills, knowledge and understanding of Unit 4 in relation to what you need to do in Part A and Part B of your set task (see also the introduction on page iii). It includes guidance and support for the following:

Revision task 1 – Guided
Part A: · **Planning the 18 hours allocated to Part A** (page 97).
- **Analysing Article 1** and making **notes** (pages 98–104).
- **Searching** for **secondary research sources, analysing** them and **making notes** (pages 104–118).
- **Preparing** for Part B using your work in Part A (page 119).

Part B: · **Answering four questions** based on Article 1 and your Part A research (pages 120–128).

Revision task 2
The opportunity to apply what you have learned in Revision task 1 to **Article 2** on a different research issue (pages 129–141).

Revision task 1

Select **either** Article 1 **or** Article 2.

> - Article 1: Health research: How to successfully implement a school-based health promotion programme (pages 98–100).
> - Article 2: Social care research: Cheap Alzheimer's drug 'may help keep people out of care homes' (pages 129–131).

This Workbook uses Article 1 in Revision task 1: How to successfully implement a school-based health promotion programme, to demonstrate one way that you can:
- **for Part A:** analyse an article, carry out secondary research related to the issue and make notes
- **for Part B:** use your research from Part A to answer four questions in your supervised assessment.

You could use this as an example for approaches to **Revision task 2** and **Article 2** on ways of keeping people with Alzheimer's out of care homes.

In your actual set task, you will be provided with set task information and you have to choose a **health** article or a **social care** article. The choice and focus of research articles will vary each year. Examples given on the Pearson website are: Article 1: Health research: Blood test could provide an early arthritis warning, and Article 2: Social care research: Employment support for disabled people: investigating the relationship between investment and outcomes.

Part A

✎ Plan your time

You need to make a plan for the 18 hours you have available for research in Part A.

Complete the table below, which reflects the eight stages of planning in this revision task, with an estimate of the time you need. You could break the timing down further.

Plan for effective use of time for Part A, 18 hours

1 Read and annotate my chosen article (page 98)	4 hrs
2 Familiarise myself with the article, making notes and identifying issues (page 101)	
3 Note keywords on identified issues, in order to search for secondary research sources (page 104)	
4 Search for and note possible sources for secondary research related to the issues in the article (page 105)	....
5 Assess reliability of Secondary research source 1, chosen with reference to Source, Appearance, Method, Timeliness, Applicability and Balance (SAMTAB) and the four Part B questions (page 107)	
6 Make notes on Secondary research source 1, including methods, reliability, ethics, importance of issue, further research (e.g. proposal, timing, ethics), impact of research on practice and provision. Show how this source links to Article 1 (page 110)	....
7 Assess reliability of Secondary research source 2 and make notes (see 5 and 6 above) (page 114)	....
8 Organise my Part A notes to take into my Part B assessment – six sides of A4 for use with Questions 1–4, including a list of my secondary research sources (page 118)	....

✏ 1 Read and annotate the article you have chosen

Pages 98–118 of this Workbook demonstrate how you can analyse a provided article, carry out your own secondary research, and make notes for use in Part B. This is based on **Article 1: How to successfully implement a school-based health promotion programme**, below.

Read Article 1 and the annotations. Add your own. Complete the notes under 'Familiarise yourself with Article 1' starting on page 101. Use the notes and analysis provided to guide you.

Article 1: Health research

How to successfully implement a school-based health promotion programme

Published on 1 March 2016

There are four broad areas to consider when implementing school-based health promotion programmes: preparing for implementation, introducing a programme within a school, embedding a programme into routine practice, and fidelity of implementation and programme adaptation. This review identified specific factors for success for each. This was based on 22 studies (some of them NIHR-funded) around health promotion interventions in UK schools. Common factors that improved the chances of successful implementation included engaging pupils, teachers and senior staff, explaining the value of the intervention in relevant terms, having a specific coordinator to support staff, and enabling staff to discuss and resolve implementation issues. A wide range of health promotion programmes were considered, including healthy eating, smoking, alcohol consumption and accidental injuries.

> Introduces issues and importance – the need to improve school-based intervention programmes

The findings give pragmatic evidence-based advice on how best to implement school-based programmes. This has potential to minimise money being wasted because of the poor implementation of programmes known to work. It will be particularly helpful for school nurses and others.

> Brief indication of findings

> Possible implications/ impact if research findings are followed

Why was this study needed?

The risk of developing many common diseases in the UK can be lowered by making lifestyle changes. For example, reducing salt intake to reduce the risk of heart disease or maintaining a healthy weight to reduce the risk of diabetes.

> Purpose of research, importance of issue, impact on practice

Many suggest that promoting healthy lifestyle choices – health promotion – should start early in life to help establish healthy habits early and prevent disease, rather than trying to reverse unhealthy habits later in life, or once illness has occurred. As such, school is recognised by NICE as an important setting for improving various aspects of health promotion, such as preventing excess weight gain, improving oral health and reducing smoking and alcohol use.

This review investigated the factors that contributed to the successful or unsuccessful implementation of UK school-based health promotion programmes.

> What research was about

What did this study do?

This was a 'realist' review – meaning it focused on the implementation of interventions, rather than their effectiveness. The first part of the review used 22 UK-based studies (some funded by NIHR) to produce a framework of the different aspects of implementation, known as 'programme theories'. These programme theories were then tested and refined using a further 41 studies. Data were extracted until

> Methods supporting reliability of results, with a triangulation of methods used (22 studies followed by testing on a further 41 studies)

> Qualitative method – 'realist' / 'programme theories'

"theoretical saturation", the point at which adding new studies is considered unlikely to yield further insight. Studies were also critically appraised so that the authors could indicate the quality of the evidence underlying their findings.

What did it find?

The review identified four 'programme theories' affecting implementation success: preparing for implementation, introducing a programme within a school, embedding a programme into routine practice and fidelity of implementation (how closely the reality matched the intention) and programme adaptation.

- **Preparing.** Integration was more likely to be successful when systematically planned in line with the school's existing responsibilities. This involved pre-delivery consultation. New or contentious programmes may need more consultation than well-established or uncontentious programmes. Pupils need to understand the relevance and benefits, and teachers and pupils need to feel supported. The authors identified the notion of reciprocity, with both teachers and pupils needing clear benefits (including non-health advantages, such as developing transferable skills) to participate. The new programme should be fitted in with current school activities.

- **Introducing.** Successful implementation was more likely if health promotion programmes are integrated into the life of the school. This can be achieved through appropriate senior level support, a named coordinator showing leadership, and positive engagement with teachers, public and others involved in the programme delivery or participation.

- **Embedding.** There was limited evidence informing how to best embed a programme into routine practice.

- **Implementing.** Limited evidence also informed best approaches to ensure fidelity – i.e. how closely the programme stuck to the original aims. But elements to consider were around programme adaptation, and the elements of the programme that are essential, optional and adaptable by those delivering it.

What does current guidance say on this issue?

NICE guidelines relating to health promotion programmes in schools cover: alcohol interventions (PH7), physical activity for children and young people (PH17), smoking prevention in schools (PH23) and social and emotional wellbeing in primary education (PH12) and secondary education (PH20). Where implementation advice is provided, it reflects the findings of this review. For example, using a 'whole school' approach to embed programmes into the school, family and wider community – such as in the case of oral health programmes (2014), smoking prevention (2010) and alcohol consumption (2007).

What are the implications?

The focus in research can often – and understandably – be on the effectiveness of an intervention, rather than how it can be best implemented in different contexts. Both are important for success. This review suggests implementation issues to consider when selecting and planning the implementation of health promotion programmes in schools. For instance, it may be helpful to identify which parts of a programme are standard and which could be adapted to fit the needs of local schools. The 'programme theories' developed in this review should be considered by those implementing programmes to maximise the chance of successful implementation and minimise the possibility of wasting resources through poor and non-evidence-based implementation.

Qualitative method – 'theoretical saturation' – supporting reliability of results

Findings of research – identified 4 programme theories – breakdown may be useful when comparing other research with this study

Importance of issue and reliability – guidance that backs up research findings, making the study more robust

Conclusion – recommendations for further research and implications on practice and provision – e.g. not possible to design 'one size fits all' approach but to have standardised aspects that are built on to fit with local needs

Possible issue for further research – combining research on individual 'local needs' with the standardised approach of the 'programme theories'

https://discover.dc.nihr.ac.uk/portal/article/4000333/how-to-successfully-implement-a-school-based-health-promotion-programme

Citation and funding

Pearson M, Chilton R, Wyatt K, et al. (2015) Implementing health promotion programmes in schools: a realist systematic review of research and experience in the United Kingdom. *Implement Sci*, 10(1):149.

This project was funded by the National Institute for Health Research, School for Public Health Research.

Bibliography

NICE, (2015) Preventing excess weight gain. NG7. London: National Institute for Health and Care Excellence.

NICE, (2014) Oral health: local authorities and partners. PH55. London: National Institute for Health and Care Excellence.

NICE, (2010) Smoking prevention in schools. PH23. London: National Institute for Health and Care Excellence.

NICE, (2009) Physical activity for children and young people. PH17. London: National Institute for Health and Care Excellence.

NICE, (2008) Social and emotional wellbeing in primary education. PH12. London: National Institute for Health and Care Excellence.

NICE, (2009) Social and emotional wellbeing in secondary education. PH20. London: National Institute for Health and Care Excellence.

NICE, (2007) Alcohol: school-based interventions. PH7. London: National Institute for Health and Care Excellence.

Authors have cited the actual research study – maybe read it, if time

NIHR may be useful source for secondary research sources

May be interesting links for secondary research sources – start with most recent

✏ 2 Familiarise yourself with Article 1

As you read Article 1, analyse it and make notes.

Complete the notes below for Article 1 on pages 98–100. The six questions can be used to structure notes on any research piece. Some notes have been started below for you, based on one person's response to the article. Refer to the article and notes, and add your own thoughts.

Notes on Article 1: National Institute for Health Research (NIHR) (2016) How to successfully implement a school-based health promotion programme. [Online] Available: https://discover.dc.nihr.ac.uk/portal/article/4000333/how-to-successfully-implement-a-school-based-health-promotion-programme [22 Oct 2016]

1   What was the research piece about? (e.g. what it explored, why it was important, what the study aimed to find out)

This research piece was about exploring how well health promotion programmes were implemented in schools. The study looked at a number of interventions that had been implemented in the UK.

> Complete the notes about what the research piece was about. Consider the purpose in finding common themes that increased the chances of the positive implementation of programmes that would benefit children's health early in their lives. Why was the research issue considered important and what could it result in? What did the research questions aim to find out?

The purpose was to find out ....

....

....

....

....

....

....

....

....

....

....

....

....

....

> For Part B, it is important to understand the research focus, in order to inform your understanding of methods and reliability in Question 1. The importance of the issues is a key focus of Question 2.

2 What were the key methods used in the research? (e.g. qualitative, quantitative, mixed; how they supported the reliability of the research)

This research used a 'realist' review method. This is a qualitative approach that develops 'programme theories'. In this case, it looked at the model of intervention, possible outcomes and activities that led to the outcomes. It reviewed 22 studies to produce a framework (programme theories) to explore the different aspects of the way the intervention programmes were implemented. It also used a saturation method, using a further 41 studies until it came to the point where no new insights were becoming apparent from these studies. Theoretical saturation is an approach used in analysing qualitative data. Here, the researcher continues to sample and analyse data until no new data appears and the ideas in the study or theory are well defined.

> The notes above identify and explain the **qualitative methods** of **realistic review** and **saturation method**, so that readers understand them. The notes show understanding of **data usage**. When looking at methods used in research, remember that some articles may not say whether the methods are qualitative, quantitative or mixed. Remember: numbers and charts are likely to be quantitative; words, language and speech are likely to be qualitative. Numbers/charts/words/ language may be mixed methods.
>
> Complete the notes below with a comment on reliability. To do this, use the notes around the article on using a **triangulation** of methods. Assess whether you think the triangulation of methods has been useful and if it is likely to produce reliable results.
>
> Methods and reliability of results are a key focus in Part B, Question 1.

The methods support reliable outcomes because ....

....

....

....

....

3 What were the key findings in the research? (e.g. what were the results of the study? Did they answer the research questions? What were the conclusions/importance of the issues?)

Through reviewing the 41 studies and testing the programme theories, the researchers identified four 'programme theories' they felt led to success in school-based programmes. These findings were:

1 ....

....

2 & 3: Introducing and embedding. If the programmes were introduced and embedded to fit with the

schools' values and principles, it ....

4 ....

....

The researchers discuss how current guidelines for health promotion programmes in schools link with specific health issues, e.g. alcohol, physical activity, smoking. They also note how advice given reinforces the findings in this study. They recommend that the four identified programme theories should be used in future programmes to increase the chances of successful intervention.

> - Key findings and reliability of results are a key focus in Part B, Question 1.
> - Importance of the issue, conclusions and effects on individuals are a key focus in Question 2.
> - Implications for future research are a key focus in Question 3.
> - Implications for practice and provision are a key focus in Question 4.

4 Were any recommendations/future research plans discussed? (e.g. do they recommend further research? Did any aspects of the research not go well? Consider proposal, methods, reliability, research skills required, ethical considerations, timescales.)

This research found that there were links between programme theories and current guidelines that provide advice for specific intervention programmes, such as those concerning alcohol, diet, obesity (NICE, 2015, 2014, 2010, 2009 (a) (b), 2008, 2007). The study suggested that, by exploring how programmes were implemented and how they could take account of the individual needs of the schools, those implementing programmes would be more effective in promoting a successful intervention. It recommends that further research should use the programme theories when planning interventions. This may help developers to tailor-make programmes that fit the needs of individual schools while retaining standardised elements.

> - The notes correctly cite the NICE guidelines, using date order from most recent dates and (a) (b) when there are two from the same year, so that they can be referred to separately if necessary. The answer correctly identifies possibilities for future research (ways of tailoring the programme to meet individual school needs), along with recommended approaches (using the framework of the 'programme theories') in order to achieve successful outcomes which use resources well (which can save money).
> - You could go on to give a brief example of future research into individual school needs that could be met by tailoring the intervention programme theories, bearing in mind ethical considerations and timelines. Use tentative language such as 'could', 'might' and 'suggests', which is appropriate in a research context.
> - Planning and ethical considerations for further research is a key focus in Question 3.

For example, a useful piece of future research might be to ....

....

....

....

....

....

5 What could be the implications/impact on my practice? (e.g. how can this type of research affect individuals in my workplace? How will it affect my own practice?)

The research findings of this study are useful because they show ways to successfully implement programmes in schools. They provide a framework to follow (from using the programme theories) which could be adapted to suit the needs of any school.

> - To continue the notes, you could comment on how you could develop and tailor a programme to target individual needs at school. You could consider possible positive/negative effects and the reasons for them. You could consider how using a good existing framework might save time and development costs. You could note how interventions that fit with existing school policies might be more successful in supporting children's healthy life choices and chances, and give an example.
> - Research implications for future practice are a key focus in Question 4.

This would have a positive impact on my practice because it would give me ....

....

....

....

....

<u>6 What could be the implications/impact on service provision? (e.g. what are the wider implications on society, and on the cost and effectiveness of service providers?)</u>

> Your notes could comment on how intervention programmes like this would have a positive impact on service provision. You could consider the reduction in costs of tailor-made programmes by specialist staff. You could note that if the programmes are introduced early in children's lives, it will have a positive impact on their adult health needs, reducing obesity, drug addiction and misuse of alcohol, for example, saving costs to the health service. In this way you are considering the immediate impact on cost savings, and also the future impact and savings.

....

....

....

....

....

....

....

....

> Research implications for future provision are a key focus in Question 4.

 Links To revise ways of approaching the research process, see the following pages of the Revision Guide.

- Pages 168–171 to revise the purposes, issues, rationale and planning for research.
- Pages 172–182 to revise research methods, ethical issues and confidentiality.
- Pages 183–193 to revise research skills including notes, records and referencing techniques, and searching for and selecting appropriate secondary sources.
- Pages 194–199 to revise evaluation of research, including bias and interpretation in research.
- Pages 200–203 to revise future research, recommendations and implications for practice and provision.

Guided

 3 Note keywords for searching for secondary sources

You are required to identify at least **two** secondary research sources related to the issue in the provided article, and make notes. The bibliography and source for **Article 1** are good places to start.

You could also use simple **internet keyword searches** such as: *partnership, working together, health and social care collaboration.*

You can also use Boolean operators in your search. For example: **And** brings up all terms you type in (e.g. schools **and** interventions); **Or** brings up **either** schools **or** intervention; **Not** brings up schools **not** interventions. If you use * after a word it will bring up all possible extensions (e.g. partner* will bring up partnership, partners).

Using the bibliography contained in Article 1 (page 100), note four possible keywords you could use for an internet search for secondary sources. Two have been suggested for you.

<u>Notes on keywords for an internet search for secondary sources, based on Article 1</u>

1 Smoking prevention <u>and</u> schools

2 Childhood obesity programmes

3 ....

4 ....

4 Search for and note possible sources

When searching for sources you need to refine your search from many possibilities to at least two. It is important to include the following considerations:

- Links with the issue of research in Article 1 and the focus of the four Part B questions.
- If your sources include different research methods, you can show the ways they are effective to research the issue, their use of data, and how they have been chosen to support reliable outcomes.
- The importance of the issue for research, and ways the source includes future research considerations and the impact of research on provision and practice.
- The reliability and validity of the source, using criteria to check against (e.g. SAMTAB, page 107).
- You could search on the website of the source of Article 1 (NIHR) and other organisations involved in health research. It is good practice to make a note of key information on possible sources for reference, along with some key points to remind you of the research.

Choose at least two of the four keywords you noted on page 104 to search the internet and note possible sources. Narrow them down to at least two secondary research sources that best relate to Article 1 and the considerations above. Use the below and create any additional records you need.

Title of research piece or article ....

Name(s) of author(s) ....

Source of article (e.g. journal, webpage, government site) ....

Year of publication .... Page numbers ....

If webpage, date accessed ....

URL: ....

Some key points: what the research was about, methods, findings, links to Article 1

....

....

....

Title of research piece or article ....

Name(s) of author(s) ....

Source of article (e.g. journal, webpage, government site) ....

Year of publication .... Page numbers ....

If webpage, date accessed ....

URL: ....

Some key points: what the research was about, methods, findings, links to Article 1

....

....

....

Title of research piece or article ....

Name(s) of author(s) ....

Source of article (e.g. journal, webpage, government site) ....

Year of publication .... Page numbers ....

If webpage, date accessed ....

URL: ....

Some key points: what the research was about, methods, findings, links to Article 1

....

....

> **Links** To revise searching for sources, see pages 190–193 of the Revision Guide.

> This Workbook chooses Secondary research source 1 as noted below.

Notes on Secondary research source 1

Title of research piece: Children's body mass index, overweight and obesity

Name of author: Linda Ng Fat

Source: Health and Social Care Information Centre (HSCIC), _Health Survey for England 2014_ Vol 1, Ch 10

Year of publication: 2014, Number of pages: 10pp Date on which accessed URL: 24.10.2016

URL: http://healthsurvey.hscic.gov.uk/media/33539/HSE2014-Ch10-Child-obesity.pdf

Some key points: Rise in levels of obesity in schools; intervention programmes to tackle it; includes quantitative data (relates to research issue in provided Article 1, using different methods)

> Now complete the details for Secondary source 2, using **one of your chosen** secondary research sources.

Notes on Secondary research source 2

Title of research piece or article ....

Name(s) of author(s) ....

Source of article (e.g. journal, webpage, government site) ....

Year of publication .... Page numbers ....

If webpage, date accessed ....

URL: ....

Some key points: what the research was about, methods, findings, links to Article 1

....

....

....

✎ **5 Complete a SAMTAB and notes on Secondary research source 1**

You need to identify whether the secondary research you would like to use comes from a reputable source, as this will indicate whether it can be relied upon. You can assess the **validity** and **reliability** by completing a SAMTAB for the **S**ource, **A**ppearance, **M**ethod, **T**imeliness, **A**pplicability and **B**alance of the secondary sources you consider.

- The SAMTAB below shows you the kinds of things you can record, using Secondary research source 1 as an example, including ethical considerations
- The SAMTAB will help you to assess how Secondary research sources meet the criteria you need, so you can move forward with at least two of the most suitable sources.

There is no requirement for you to use a SAMTAB in your actual set task unless it is of use to you.

Read the guidance and entries below on Secondary research source 1. Complete the final entry on 'notes and links'. To do this, you could analyse Source 1 online or use information from the notes on pages 101–104. This information will be useful in Part B.

Assessing reliability and validity of a research source
Source, **A**ppearance, **M**ethod, **T**imeliness, **A**pplicability, **B**alance **(SAMTAB)**

RESEARCH TITLE AUTHOR SOURCE	Use a referencing format (e.g. Harvard) to also use in your Part B assessment. *Children's body mass index, overweight and obesity* *Linda Ng Fat* *Health and Social Care Information Centre (HSCIC), HSE 2014. Health Survey for England 2014 Vol 1, Ch 10* *2014, 10pp. [Online] Available at http://healthsurvey.hscic.gov.uk/media/33539/HSE2014-Ch10-Child-obesity.pdf [Accessed 22 October 2016]*
SOURCE	Does it come from a reputable source/journal (usually noted on the webpage)? Is author information included? Do you know the publisher? Note that Wikipedia may not always be considered a reliable source. *The information comes from the Health and Social Care Information Centre (HSCIC), which is the national provider of information, data and IT systems for health and social care. This is a reliable government source.*
APPEARANCE	Can you read and understand it? Does it look professionally written (e.g. correct spelling and grammar)? Some blogs may not necessarily be reliable as you may not know the credentials of the author. *The information in the article is clear and there is a good summary at the beginning that highlights the main points of the study. It is professionally written with no grammatical or other errors. The layout and appearance look professionally prepared.*
METHOD	Does it use appropriate methods for the study? Are the methods clear? How big is the study? Do the research methods support reliability of results? Is the method similar to the provided article, or different? *Examines patterns of overweight and obesity levels of children aged 2–15 using information from government health surveys (HSE). Uses quantitative measures to identify key points from surveys (different from qualitative methods in Article 1). Sources appear reliable; methods use government statistics.*
TIMELINESS	Is it up to date? It is best practice to find up-to-date material, e.g. from the last 10 years. Anything older may not be so reliable, as society, thinking and research changes. Some older sources retain relevance – e.g. Piaget's cognitive theories of the 1960s. *This article was published in 2014 and is therefore up to date. Perhaps look for more recent data to see how the current level compares to the 2014 survey.*

APPLICABILITY	Does it focus on the issues/questions you are exploring? Research may be interesting, but not relevant to the area being explored. If so, it will not add value. How does it link with your provided article? How does it link with the focus of the four questions in Part B?
	Yes, obesity is one of the areas that schools are currently trying to tackle and the HSCIC article shows that, despite intervention programmes, obesity in children still seems to be rising. The findings in Article 1 seem to support the idea of improving intervention programme strategies to help support reduction of such issues. The research in the HSCIC article includes information relating to the four Part B questions.
BALANCE	Does it give a non-judgemental view? Does the author adopt a particular standpoint? If the author gives opinions that are not backed up by research, they may be showing bias towards an issue, instead of substantiated fact.
	Yes, this article is factual and based on statistical evidence to illustrate how the level of obesity in children has changed over time. It uses government statistics from surveys of the population which drew on a large sample; therefore, there is a good level of validity.

Summarise key aspects of the study, findings, and relevance to Article 1.

Complete the notes below by referring to Secondary source 1 online or using the notes on pages 110–117. These will act as prompts.

NOTES AND LINKS

1   What the research piece is about, and importance of issues: Looks at how the levels of obesity have risen and how these changes relate to factors such as household income and gender. It illustrates the importance of school intervention programmes to help children and parents to tackle obesity.

Relationship to Article 1: links very well with Article 1 as it cites programmes such as the Healthy Child Programme that have been introduced into schools.

2   Key methods used and reliability: quantitative, because the research aimed to identify ....

....

so it used ....

....

....

Relationship to Article 1: Article 1 used qualitative methods, because the research aimed to find out

....

It used ....

showing ....

....

<u>3 Key findings and importance:</u> ....

....

....

....

....

<u>Relationship to Article 1:</u> ....

....

<u>4 Recommendations/further research, also in relation to Article 1:</u> Plan research on successful intervention programmes to reduce obesity, matched to framework of 'programmes' in Article 1. Consider project proposal, plan/timing, methods and skills needed, and ethical considerations. To help inform this, research most recent UK data on obesity.

<u>5 Implications for practice and provision:</u> ....

....

....

....

....

<u>Relationship to Article 1:</u> ....

....

....

Links To revise suitability of sources and use of a SAMTAB and ethical checklist, see page 193 of the Revision Guide.

Unit 4

Guided

Guided

---

 6 Make notes on Secondary research source 1

You need to make notes on the research sources you choose that will help you to develop answers for Part B of the set task. The notes you make should be objective and report what is written in the article. Using a computer can be a good way for you to bring together six A4 sides of organised, clear notes to use in Part B.

Read the following notes on Secondary research source 1, and the guidance in the tint boxes. Then use information from these notes and the SAMTAB on page 107 to complete the notes towards the end.

Notes on Secondary research source 1: Ng Fat, L. (2014) Children's body mass index, overweight and obesity. Health and Social Care Information Centre (HSCIC), HSE 2014. Health Survey for England 2014 Vol 1, Ch 10 [Online] Available at : http://healthsurvey.hscic.gov.uk/media/33539/HSE2014-Ch10-Child-obesity.pdf [22 October 2016]

1   What was the research piece about? (what it explored, why it was important, what the study aimed to find out)

The study was conceived by the Health and Social Care Information Centre (HSCIC) and written by Linda Ng Fat. It aimed to identify trends in overweight and obese children in England. The data was collected about children in England aged between 2 and 15 years. The report recognises that childhood obesity is now of global concern, particularly to the ongoing health and mental wellbeing of next generations. The report claims that childhood obesity is linked to heart problems, diabetes and early death, as well as psychological problems (depression, emotional and behavioural issues).

The report cites concern that childhood obesity in England has risen significantly over the past two decades despite the many government incentives to combat childhood obesity.

This links very well with Article 1, as it cites programmes such as the Healthy Child Programme that have been introduced into schools.

> The above notes give a good overview of the study. It is good practice to summarise research so you gain a good understanding of what the study was about and how it might be relevant to your chosen provided article. At the end of the paragraph, a useful link between Secondary research source 1 and Article 1 is identified.

2   What were the key methods used in the research? (e.g qualitative, quantitative, mixed; how they supported the reliability of the research)

Methods used in this study collated data from records of overweight and obese children aged 2–15 years. It looked at the trends according to age, gender and household income for the period 1995–2014. Children's desire to lose weight was collected from 2006. Children's height and weight were measured and their BMI calculated. This was a quantitative exercise, analysing data from existing records, with no qualitative or mixed methods research. The original sources seem reliable, as does the method of reviewing literature to draw conclusions about changes over time.

> The above notes identify that there were no specific methods other than analysing existing records. The final sentence notes that the research was quantitative, and did not use qualitative or mixed methods.

 Look at page 172 of the Revision Guide to revise quantitative methods, and pages 194-196 to revise interpreting and presenting quantitative data.

110

3 What were the key findings in the research? (e.g. what were the results of the study? Did they answer the research questions? What were the conclusions / importance of the issues?)

a) Overall findings: There appears to have been a significant rise in the prevalence of obesity since 1995. Although it seems to have levelled out between 2004/5 and 2014, it is still higher than in 1995.

1995: 11% of boys and 12% of girls.

2004–2005: 19% of boys and 19% of girls.

2014: 19% of boys and 16% of girls.

> You can use **text or a chart format to present statistical findings**. Presenting data in charts can be useful to aid understanding. A **bar chart (or histogram)** gives a good graphical image of changes over time. A **pie chart**, as below, gives a good pictorial representation of findings.

Prevalence of obesity among boys and girls aged 2–15

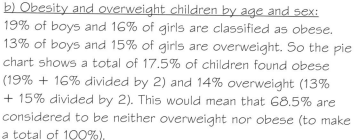

b) Obesity and overweight children by age and sex:
19% of boys and 16% of girls are classified as obese. 13% of boys and 15% of girls are overweight. So the pie chart shows a total of 17.5% of children found obese (19% + 16% divided by 2) and 14% overweight (13% + 15% divided by 2). This would mean that 68.5% are considered to be neither overweight nor obese (to make a total of 100%).

Prevalence of overweight and obesity among children aged 2–15

68.5%

17.5%   14%

☐ Neither overweight nor obese
☐ Overweight   ☐ Obese

c) Obesity and overweight by household income:
14% of children lived in households that did not provide information about income (so were excluded from the study). The proportion of boys in the lowest income quintile (any of five equal groups) who were obese was 26%, and the proportion of girls was 15% (girls' patterns for obesity were less clear). Overall, higher income households had lower proportions of overweight or obese children.

> If you are unsure of terms, look them up and add a note to remind you, as with the note on 'quintile', above.

d) Obesity and overweight by Index of Multiple Deprivation (IMD): No statistically significant variation with IMD. Author feels this may be due to chance variation as the sample size was too small to be statistically significant.

e) Children trying to change their weight: 22% of boys and 28% of girls said they were trying to lose weight. Proportionately this was greater in older children (11–15) in the sample: 24% of boys and 31% of girls.

> You could show the percentage of children trying to change their weight in a pie chart.

f) The study overall shows that, although there seems to be an increase in the level of childhood obesity from 1995–2004/5, there has been little increase since this time, which seems to be similar to other studies in England and other high-income countries. The study suggests that obesity levels may stabilise. Yet the study goes on to state that, since 2004, obesity levels in boys have peaked at 19% with girls below peak levels at around 16%. The authors also discuss other research that has shown an increase in obesity levels between 2012/13 and 2013/14.

> Paragraph (f) sums up some key findings of the entire analysis. The breakdown in the earlier paragraphs may be useful to justify any points made in recommendations, so you may wish to select some data from this section in addition to the summary when you put together your six sides of notes for Part B.

<u>4 Were any recommendations/future research plans discussed? (e.g. do they recommend further research? Did any aspects of the research not go well? Consider proposal, methods, reliability, research skills required, ethical considerations, timescales.)</u>

The author recommends that further data will be needed to monitor the changes to see if levels are reducing. This is interesting as it means that the programmes of intervention discussed in Article 1 may be working and, with further study into the programmes and making them more effective, this may help to reduce levels further. The author cites an issue that some reports show that some parents do not identify that their child is overweight/obese or they underestimate the child's weight. The study suggests that many children cannot control their food and activity choices and that levels of obesity are still high compared with children in the mid-1990s. Guidelines were published by NICE in 2015 and the author states self-monitoring and healthy choices should be encouraged, along with people eating meals together, and supporting physical activities.

Complete the notes to briefly consider a future research plan. It should include the following:
- **Types of methods and reliability**: the answer notes the need for further data, so consider sample size and availability of information, to collect and analyse further data for reliable findings.
- **Relationship to Article 1**: building on the link that has been identified, you could plan research on successful intervention programmes to reduce obesity, using a framework of theories similar to those discussed in Article 1.
- **Limitations of current research to address in future research**: the answer notes that a limitation of the study was obtaining accurate information from parents. This needs to be addressed in future research to increase reliability of findings.
- **Planning**: take into account ethical considerations such as informed consent and data protection; research skills required (those you have and those you need); possible problems and how to overcome them; timeline (e.g. updated research figures and predictions for 2020).
- **Research literature**: the answer notes further guidelines in relation to obesity and intervention, which might provide research information and links that would also relate well to Article 1.

In light of the considerations mentioned, a useful piece of future research might be to ....

....

....

....

....

....

....

....

....

....

....

....

....

🔗 **Links** To revise identifying future research, see page 202 of the Revision Guide.

5 What could be the implications/impact on my practice? (e.g. how can this type of research affect individuals in my workplace? How will it affect my own practice?)

> Use the notes in this section and the SAMTAB (page 107) to complete notes on how successful intervention programmes to reduce obesity, using the framework of 'programmes', would have a positive impact on practice. As with Article 1, you could consider how using a good existing framework might save both time and development costs. You could note how interventions that fit with existing school policies, target the specific needs of boys and girls, and influence parents, might be more successful to support children's healthy life choices and chances, and give an example.

....

....

....

....

....

....

....

....

....

6 What could be the implications/impact on service provision? (e.g. what are the wider implications on society and on the cost and effectiveness of service providers?)

> Use notes in this section and the SAMTAB (page 107) to complete notes on how successful intervention programmes to reduce obesity, using the framework of 'programmes', would have a positive impact on service provision. As with Article 1, you could consider the reduction in costs to local governments in employing specialist staff for different tailor-made programmes. You could note that, introducing programmes earlier in children's lives will have a positive impact on their future health needs when they are adults. Educating parents may also have a positive impact for a healthy weight for all the family, with this approach offering savings to health services.

....

....

....

....

....

....

....

....

....

Links Look at pages 200–201 of the Revision Guide to revise implications for provision and practice.

7 Complete a SAMTAB and notes on Secondary research source 2

Assess the **validity** and **reliability** of your chosen **Secondary research source 2**, noted on page 106, by completing a SAMTAB for the **S**ource, **A**ppearance, **M**ethod, **T**imeliness, **A**pplicability and **B**alance. Consider ethical principles too. Use the example SAMTAB on Secondary research source 1 (page 107) as a guide.

Assessing reliability and validity for Secondary research source 2	
RESEARCH TITLE AUTHOR SOURCE	Use a referencing format (e.g. Harvard) to also use in your Part B assessment. ....
SOURCE	Does it come from a reputable source/journal (usually noted on the webpage)? Is author information included? Do you know the publisher? Note that Wikipedia may not always be a reliable source. ....
APPEARANCE	Can you read it and understand it? Does it look professionally written (e.g. correct spelling and grammar?) Some sources may not necessarily be reliable as you may not know the credentials of the author. ....
METHOD	Does it use appropriate methods for the study? Are the methods clear? How big is the study? Do the research methods support reliability of results? Is the method similar to the provided article, or different? ....
TIMELINESS	Is it up to date? It is best practice to find up-to-date material, e.g. from the last 10 years. Anything older may not be so reliable, as society, thinking and research changes. Some older sources retain relevance – e.g. Piaget's cognitive theories of the 1960s. ....
APPLICABILITY	Does it focus on the issues/questions you are exploring? Research may be interesting, but not relevant to the area being explored. If so, it will not add value. How does it link with your provided article? How does it link with the focus of the four questions in Part B? ....

BALANCE	Does it give a non-judgemental view? Does the author adopt a particular standpoint? If the author gives opinions that are not backed up by research, they may be showing bias towards an issue, instead of substantiated fact.
	....
	....
	....

NOTES AND LINKS

> Summarise key aspects of the study, findings, and relevance to Article 1.
>
> Complete the notes below using your chosen Secondary research source 2. These notes will act as a prompt.

1 What research piece is about, and importance: ....

....

....

Relationship to Article 1: ....

....

2 Key methods used and reliability: ....

....

....

Relationship to Article 1: ....

....

3 Key findings and importance: ....

....

....

Relationship to Article 1: ....

....

....

4 Recommendations/further research: ....

....

....

Relationship to Article 1: ....

....

....

5 Implications for practice and provision: ....

....

....

Relationship to Article 1: ....

....

....

> **Guided**

Now complete your notes on your chosen Secondary source 2. Use the examples and comments on Article 1 (pages 98–104) and Secondary source 1 (pages 107–113) to guide you.

Notes on Secondary source 2

1 What was the research piece about? (what it explored, why it was important, what the study aimed to find out)

....

....

....

....

....

....

....

> For Part B, it is important to understand the research focus and how well the methods used have supported reliability of results. The importance of the issue for research is a key focus in Question 2.

2 What were the key methods used in the research? (e.g. qualitative, quantitative, mixed; how they supported the reliability of the research)

....

....

....

....

....

> Methods and reliability of results are a key focus in Part B, Question 1.

3 What were the key findings in the research? (e.g. what were the results of the study? Did they answer the research questions? What were the conclusions/importance of the issues?)

....

....

....

....

....

....

....

> • Key findings and reliability of results are a key focus in Part B, Question 1.
> • Importance of the issue, conclusions and effects on individuals are a key focus in Question 2.
> • Plans for future research are a key focus in Question 3.
> • Implications for practice and provision are a key focus in Question 4.

4 Were any recommendations/future research plans discussed? (e.g. do they recommend further research? Did any aspects of the research not go well? Consider proposal, methods, reliability, research skills required, ethical considerations, timescales.)

....

....

....

....

....

....

....

Planning and ethical considerations for further research is a key focus in Question 3.

5 What could be the implications/impact on my practice? (e.g. how can this type of research affect individuals in my workplace? How will it affect my own practice?)

....

....

....

....

....

....

....

Research implications for future practice are a key focus in Question 4.

6 What could be the implications/impact on service provision? (e.g. what are the wider implications on society and the cost and effectiveness of service providers?)

....

....

....

....

....

....

....

Research implications for service provision are a key focus in Question 4.

Guided

8 Organise your Part A notes to take into your Part B assessment

In your Part B supervised assessment you will be asked questions relating to the provided article and your own secondary research sources. Suggestions for how you might allocate the three hours are noted below (in brackets). You have 3 hours and you will be asked four questions that focus on:

1 understanding **research methods** and the validity and **reliability of results** in research (15 marks; 40 minutes)

2 understanding the **relationship** between **your own secondary research** and the **provided article**, and how this relationship reinforces the **importance of the issue** (15 marks; 40 minutes)

3 **planning** and **ethical considerations** for **further research** (15 marks; 40 minutes)

4 research **implications** for future **provision** and/or **practice** (20 marks; 50 minutes).

You will also list the secondary sources you have used (10 mins). At the end of the assessment you will submit your completed taskbook. Your prepared notes do not need to be submitted.

Organise your **six sides of A4 notes** in a way that best works for you to answer the Part B questions. The example below is for your notes on the secondary sources used in this revision task.

Make sure your Part A notes include the following content:

☐ your secondary sources using a recognised reference system (e.g. Harvard)

Secondary source 1:

Ng Fat, L. (2014) Children's body mass index, overweight and obesity. Health and Social Care Information Centre (HSCIC), HSE 2014. *Health Survey for England 2014* Vol 1, Ch 10 [Online] Available: http://healthsurvey.hscic.gov.uk/media/33539/HSE2014-Ch10-Child-obesity.pdf [22 Oct 2016]

Secondary source 2 (note the reference for your secondary source from page 106):

....

....

....

....

....

Your notes on Article 1, Secondary research source 1, Secondary research source 2:

☐ What the research piece was about (what it explored and aimed to find out).

☐ Key research methods used (including validity and reliability of results).

☐ Key findings in the research (results of the study; how they answered the research questions).

☐ Recommendations for future research (including planning and ethical considerations).

☐ Implications for practice and provision (on individuals and society).

☐ Links showing the relationship between the secondary research and Article 1.

Select from your Part A notes to create six sides of A4 notes with information about each of the three research sources. Consider using a computer to ensure that they are clear and legible.

Links Notes for Article 1 start on page 98, Secondary source 1 on page 107, Secondary source 2 on page 114.

Part B

For this revision task, to answer the four questions in Part B, you will need to refer to your preparation and six sides of A4 notes from Part A on:
- Article 1: How to successfully implement a school-based health promotion programme
- Secondary research source 1: Children's body mass index, overweight and obesity
- Secondary research source 2: Your chosen researched secondary source

SECTION 1: HEALTH RESEARCH

Article 1: How to successfully implement a school-based health promotion programme

Provide a list of the secondary sources you have used in addition to Article 1.

Refer to the list of secondary sources you have prepared, using the same recognised referencing system (e.g. Harvard) you used in Part A, and list them here. When giving research sources:
- list them in alphabetical order. If two references start with the same letter, list them in date order with the most recent date first
- where an acronym is used, cite the full name and the acronym in brackets the first time it is used. You can then just use the acronym e.g. Health and Social Care Information Centre (HSCIC)

As a guide, spend no more than **10 minutes** listing your secondary sources, prepared in your Part A notes.

> **Guided** **1** How has qualitative research been used to extract data in this article and other articles you have researched about the issue?

In your answer you should include:

(a) what other methods of research have been used to explore the issue

(b) how reliable the results of the research methods used are.

15 marks

As a guide, spend about **40 minutes** answering Question 1. Complete the guided answer below – this reflects one way of structuring an answer.

In your answer, show your understanding of research methods and the validity and reliability of results of the research. For example:
* explain the research methods and show your understanding of data usage
* support your evaluative judgements on suitability
* show your understanding of other research methods used to explore the issue
* support your conclusions on reliability, showing an understanding of the concept in the context of the methods used.

In Article 1, the research was about how well health promotion programmes were implemented in schools. The study looked at a number of interventions that had been implemented in the UK to assess success. The research by NIHR (2016) reports that the research conducted by Pearson, Chilton, Wyatt et al. (2015) used a 'realist' review method. This is a qualitative approach that develops 'programme theories'. In this case, it looked at the model of intervention, possible outcomes and activities that led to the outcomes. It reviewed 22 studies to produce a framework (programme theories) to explore the different aspects of the way the intervention programmes were implemented. It also used a saturation method using a further 41 studies until it came to the point where no further insights were becoming apparent from these studies. Theoretical saturation is an approach used in analysing qualitative data, when the researcher continues to sample and analyse data until no new data appears and the ideas in the study or theory are well defined. The methods support reliable outcomes through using a triangulation of methods and referring to a range of current guidance on the issue.

* This answer refers to the notes prepared in Part A. It starts by briefly introducing what the research issue was about, quickly moving on to identifying the qualitative research methods. It explains what the qualitative research methods used in Article 1 were, why they were suitable and how they support reliable results.
* You could go on to write about the quantitative methods used in Secondary research source 1. Refer to the notes you prepared in Part A. You could comment that the author collected data from various research sources and the methods looked at existing data, statistics and research on obesity over time. You could comment on the presentation of quantitative measures using percentages to explore the issue and present findings, along with the method of reviewing research literature to gain understanding of how levels of obesity change over time. Consider how the sources chosen by the author appear reliable but apply caution, for example by stating that 'methods used may be reliable because they are based on…' Comment on any issues that may have affected results, such as the need for increased data.

The research methods that were used in the report *Children's body mass index, overweight and obesity* (HSCIC, 2014) were quantitative in that the author reported on data collected from various sources of instances of obesity in England since 1995. The source ....

....

....

....

....

....

....

....

When explaining research methods, you could present data visually to aid understanding. You could show how these support conclusions on the reliability of the methods used. You could go on to write about the research methods used in your Secondary research source 2 and how reliable the results of the research methods are, referring to the notes you prepared in Part A.

....

....

....

....

....

....

....

....

....

....

Your conclusion could sum up how reliable the results of the research methods used in the secondary research sources are, and advantages and disadvantages in relation to Article 1 and the issue.

....

....

....

....

....

Links Look at pages 172–176 of the Revision Guide to revise research methods and pages 209–211 to revise approaches to Question 1.

Total for Question 1 = 15 marks

Guided 2 Why is research that leads to more effective implementation of school-based health promotion programmes important for individuals?

In your answer to this question you should include how far your secondary research supports the conclusions drawn in the article.

`15 marks`

> As a guide, spend about **40 minutes** answering Question 2. Complete the guided answer below – this reflects one way of structuring an answer.
>
> In your answer, show your understanding of the relationship between your own secondary research and the provided article, and how this relationship reinforces the importance of the issue. For example:
> * analyse the issue, leading to conclusions about the issue's importance
> * provide relevant examples of effects on individuals, supported by research findings
> * explain the relationship between your secondary research findings and the issue in the article
> * show your understanding of the relationship between the two.

The research in Article 1 conducted by Pearson, Chilton, Wyatt et al. (2015) illustrates how implementing successful healthy promotion programmes can have a positive effect on reducing the risks associated with children later developing common diseases such as heart disease and diabetes. It is important in today's society to help children and parents understand the effects of ....

....

....

....

....

The research findings suggest the need to identify parts of the programme which can be adapted to fit the needs of individual schools. This would result in a targeted approach that ....

....

> This answer starts by drawing on the Part A notes on what the research is about, the importance of the issue for individuals, and the findings and conclusions of the research in Article 1. Make sure you include source references so the reader knows what you are referring to. This answer includes references to Pearson, Chilton, Wyatt et al. (2015) above and Ng Fat (2014), below.
>
> You could go on to include why research like this is important for individuals (e.g. service users such as children and parents, and colleagues) and how far your secondary research supports the conclusions in Article 1. You could draw on some of the data of the findings from secondary sources to justify your comments.

In my secondary research I have found that over time the prevalence of obesity has increased

(Ng Fat, 2014), so research such as this will help to improve ....

For example, Figure 1 shows that over the last two decades ....

....

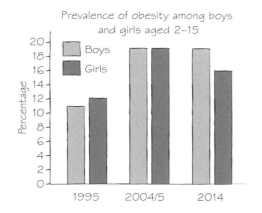

Figure 1: Changes in obesity levels since 1995

....

....

....

....

Remember to refer to **both** your secondary research sources and show **how far they support the conclusions in Article 1** about why research like this is important for individuals. Provide examples and facts from the research to support your objective response. For example, research in both Article 1 and Secondary source 1 shows the importance of intervention programmes that best target specific needs to improve individual outcomes. Consider how Secondary research source 2 relates to these conclusions and give any examples.

....

....

....

....

....

....

....

Your conclusion could sum up how far your secondary resources support the conclusions in Article 1 about why research like this is important for individuals, and comment on the reliability of any differing conclusions.

....

....

....

....

Links Look at page 169 of the Revision Guide to revise issues in health and social care, page 192 for relationships between sources and pages 212–213 for approaches to Question 2.

Total for Question 2 = 15 marks

Guided >

3 You are planning to carry out further research into the way that intervention programmes for health promotion in schools are implemented. What will you need to consider when planning this research?

In your answer you should refer to the article and to your own secondary research.

15 marks

> As a guide, spend about **40 minutes** answering Question 3. Complete the guided answer below – this reflects one way of structuring an answer.
>
> In your answer, show your understanding of planning and ethical considerations for further research, supporting any judgements made. For example:
> • suggest research methods that could be used to continue investigation/exploration into the issue and give your reasons why
> • show your understanding of why the methods chosen are effective and suitable, and justify the choices
> • show your analysis skills
> • cover the planning considerations, ethical issues and necessary research skills required to explore the issue, showing your understanding of the practical problems involved in conducting research.

Pearson, Chilton, Wyatt et al.'s study (2015) highlighted the importance of implementing successful intervention programmes in schools to support prevention of common diseases. The study suggested that exploring how programmes were implemented and whether they take account of schools' individual needs would be effective in promoting the success of an intervention. A limitation of the research that was mentioned, was ....

....

In light of that, further research could ....

....

My secondary research included exploration into the incidence of obesity and its increase

since 1995 (Ng Fat, 2014). The author noted a limitation that ....

This is interesting as it means that future research could ....

....

> This answer starts by drawing on notes from Part A to outline future research needs, including ways to address the limitations of current research identified by the researchers of Article 1 and Secondary source 1, and what this might mean for your future research plans. You could go on to draw on your notes from Part A on future research needs and plans resulting from Secondary research source 2.

My secondary research also included ....

....

....

> You could move on to outline your overall future research plan. Make sure you justify your research plan to continue the exploration into the issue. Include planning considerations of the research methods and reliability, research skills you have and those you need, and timescales to complete a piece of research.

To address this, I would conduct further research using mixed methods, particularly into ....

....

....

....

I would need to design a research study that would extend or test the recommendations made. My

plan would be to ....

....

....

> As you continue, justify how your decisions on methods are suitable for reliable outcomes.

I would use both quantitative and qualitative methods (mixed methods). I would implement and

observe the programme ....

....

....

I would also send questionnaires to parents about ....

....

For the quantitative aspect, I would be establishing data such as how many ....

....

> Go on to take account of ethical considerations, justifying how your decisions are suitable and effective for reliable outcomes (e.g. informed consent, permission to use settings, mental and physical capacity, data protection, legislation, recognised code of ethical conduct). Also, consider any practical problems you may encounter in your research and how to overcome them.

It is important to ensure ethical procedures are followed so that participants do not experience

harm or unfair treatment, and are not asked leading questions or given incorrect information. Ethical

issues that I would need to consider for this research would be ....

....

....

....

> Your conclusion could sum up possible strengths and limitations of your research plans.

....

....

....

....

Links Look at pages 170–176 of the Revision Guide to revise planning research, pages 177–182 for ethical considerations, page 202 for identifying future research and pages 214–216 for approaches to Question 3.

Total for Question 3 = 15 marks

> **Guided** > 4   What implications does this research have for practice and/or the provision of health services for children?

In your answer you should refer to the article and your own secondary research.

`20 marks`

As a guide, spend about **50 minutes** answering Question 4. Complete the guided answer below – this reflects one way of structuring an answer.

In your answer, show your understanding of research implications for future provision and/or practice. For example:
- analyse and explain the implications of the research for provision/practice in the sector in a clear, orderly way
- show your understanding of the implications of the issue in the context of the article and wider research
- justify your recommendations for change
- give supported reasons for any implications.

The research conducted by Pearson, Chilton, Wyatt et al. (2015) suggests that developing programmes aimed at health promotion can have a positive impact on reducing the risk of children developing common diseases and could be most successful when linked to individual needs. The HSCIC study (2014) further emphasises how obesity has risen since 1995. It supports the conclusions on the importance of developing interventions that are more effective in tackling such health issues. Such interventions will have a significant positive impact on the cost of health services in providing support and treatments, as well as improving children's health and wellbeing overall.

This answer shows how findings from Article 1 and Secondary source 1 could impact on provision of children's health and wellbeing overall, drawing on your Part A notes. Move on to show the implications of Secondary source 2.

My further secondary research ....

....

....

....

....

- Now go into more detail to analyse and explain the implications of your research for provision and/or practice, drawing on your notes in Part A.
- Consider how the different aspects of research might break down into important parts, and address implications for practice and provision for each one, systematically. For example, details from the Secondary source 1 research findings on obesity may influence decisions for future practice and provision.
- Also draw on your knowledge of practice in and provision of health services for children, in the context of the research sources and wider research.

Remember to fully support the implications you suggest by including references to all sources, giving reasons and examples.

....

....

....

....

....

....

....

....

....

....

....

....

....

....

> You could consider possible **advantages and disadvantages** of the implications of the research on practice and provision. Give specific **examples** of some possible **advantages** of targeted health programmes for schools, for example, reduced costs to health services (why? how?), changes in provision as a result of healthy life choices for children and their future (in what ways?) and influences on parents (how?).

....

....

....

....

....

....

....

....

....

....

> To balance advantages, give examples of **possible disadvantages**, such as possible negative reactions against the health programmes, with some children and parents not wanting to be told what to do and continuing with unhealthy lifestyle choices. This might result in wasted time and money. What are the implications for practice and provision to avoid this?

....

....

....

....

....

....

....

You could move on, considering these implications, to summarise key recommendations for changes to practice and provision, making sure you justify your recommendations.

....

....

....

....

....

....

....

....

....

....

....

....

....

....

....

....

....

Links Look at pages 200 and 201 of the Revision Guide to revise implications of research for practice and for the provision of services, and pages 217–218 to revise approaches to Question 4.

Total for Question 4 = 20 marks

END OF REVISION TASK

TOTAL FOR REVISION TASK = 65 marks

Revision task 2

 You could use Article 2 below to carry out your own analysis and secondary research into related issues, using the examples from Article 1 to guide you.

Part A

For Part A you have 18 hours to prepare, research, and create up to six sides of notes for use in your Part B supervised assessment. You will need to:

- understand the requirements of the Task Brief and plan your time (see page 97)
- read and analyse Article 2, making notes (see pages 98–104 for guidance and examples based on Article 1)
- search for and locate two related Secondary research sources, assessing them for reliability, validity and ethical considerations – you could use a SAMTAB (**S**ource, **A**ppearance, **M**ethod, **T**imeliness, **A**pplicability and **B**alance table) (see pages 101–118 for guidance and examples based on the research subject of Article 1)
- organise your notes in a way that is most useful to apply to the four questions you will be asked in Part B (see page 118).

Part B

For Part B you will need to:

- list your secondary sources on page 132 (see guidance and examples on page 119)
- answer the four Part B questions on pages 133–141, drawing on your notes from Part A (see pages 98–106 for guidance and examples based on Article 1).

Part A

Article 2: Social care research: Cheap Alzheimer's drug 'may help keep people out of care homes'

Tuesday October 27 2015

The drug, donepezil, is reported to cost 6p for a daily course

'Alzheimer's drug may keep late-stage sufferers out of nursing homes,' *The Guardian* reports. A study found people with Alzheimer's who continued to take a drug called donepezil were less likely to be admitted into care than people who stopped taking it.

Donepezil is usually withdrawn as a treatment for people with moderate to severe Alzheimer's disease as it had been thought to provide little benefit.

In this study, researchers wanted to see if this was a hasty decision and people should actually continue to take the drug – they carried out a randomised controlled study to look at the issue.

People with moderate to severe Alzheimer's, who were living in the community, were randomly allocated to discontinue or continue taking donepezil, either in combination with another Alzheimer's drug called memantine, or switching to memantine alone.

The main outcome the researchers looked at was whether these people ended up being placed in a nursing home. The results showed discontinuing donepezil roughly doubled the chance of nursing home placements during the first year. There was no significant difference between these groups in the following three years.

This study cannot prove donepezil was directly responsible for keeping people from being admitted to nursing homes. It examined the effects of continued donepezil treatment on nursing home placement – not on cognitive function. But the researchers did speculate donepezil could help people with Alzheimer's cope better with day-to-day tasks, such as dressing.

Guidelines for the best practice for treating Alzheimer's continue to evolve, so it is likely these results will feed into that process.

Where did the story come from?

The study was carried out by researchers from various different UK institutions, including University College London, King's College London, Oxford Health NHS Foundation Trust, the University of Leicester, the University of Edinburgh, Five Boroughs Partnership NHS Foundation Trust, the Centre for Ageing and Vitality (Newcastle upon Tyne), the University of Manchester, the University of Nottingham, and the University of Southampton.

It was funded by the Medical Research Council and the UK Alzheimer's Society, and was published in the peer-reviewed *The Lancet Neurology*.

The researchers declared that all the drugs and placebo were provided by Pfizer-Eisai and Lundbeck, but the pharmaceutical companies had no involvement in the design or conduct of the study, or the analysis or reporting of the data.

The researchers also declared they received payments from various different major pharmaceutical companies that specialise in drugs related to central nervous system diseases for work unrelated to this study.

The UK media's reporting of this study was accurate and balanced. *The Daily Telegraph* reported that, although the drug was originally licensed for only mild and moderate dementia, based on the results of a trial in 2012, the National Institute for Health and Care Excellence (NICE) told doctors they are free to continue prescribing donepezil in the later stages of the disease. But many GPs stop prescribing the medication because of its side effects, which include nausea and an irregular heartbeat.

Many news sources discuss the potential economic implications of the study, pointing out that a year's worth of donepezil costs around £21 a year, compared with a year's worth of care home costs – estimated to be between £30,732 and £34,424 a year. If the results of the study were replicated at a population level, this could save the NHS a considerable sum of money.

What kind of research was this?

This randomised, double-blind, placebo-controlled study assessed the impact of continuing or discontinuing the Alzheimer's drug donepezil on nursing home placement in people with moderate to severe Alzheimer's disease.

Alzheimer's disease is the most common cause of dementia. The word *dementia* describes a set of symptoms that can include memory loss and difficulties with thinking, problem solving or language. According to the Alzheimer's Society, there are more than 520,000 people with Alzheimer's disease in the UK.

Donepezil, commonly sold under the brand name Aricept, is a drug licensed to treat mild to moderate Alzheimer's disease, along with the alternative drugs galantamine and rivastigmine. It's recommended that cognitive function is assessed after three months to give an indication of how well the drug is working.

Another drug called memantine has a slightly different mechanism of action and is licensed for the treatment of moderate to severe Alzheimer's. The researchers looked at discontinuing or continuing donepezil, either alone or in combination with memantine, or switching to memantine alone.

What did the research involve?

This study included a total of 295 individuals (average age 77 years) living in the community in England and Scotland between 2008 and 2010, and who were receiving specialist care for their Alzheimer's.

People were included in the study if they had moderate or severe Alzheimer's disease and had been prescribed donepezil continuously for at least three months at a dose of 10mg for at least the previous six weeks.

All participants in the study had a score of between 5 and 13 on the Mini-Mental State Examination (MMSE). This is a standardised screening test used to evaluate cognitive impairment in older adults.

Individuals were excluded if they had severe or unstable medical disorders, were receiving memantine, or had been deemed unlikely to adhere to the study regimens.

They were assigned to one of four treatment groups for one year:

- Group one – continue donepezil
- Group two – discontinue donepezil
- Group three – discontinue donepezil and start taking memantine
- Group four – continue donepezil and start taking memantine

All people took two drugs each day, combining a placebo for the respective drug when it wasn't given so participants and assessors were unaware of which group they had been allocated to – for example, donepezil with memantine placebo.

Place of residence was recorded during the first year of the trial and then every six months for the next three years.

What were the basic results?

Out of the total of 295 study participants, 162 (55%) were admitted to a nursing home within four years of the start of the trial.

In brief, the researchers found the groups who discontinued donepezil had a roughly doubled chance of nursing home placement during the first year, compared with those who continued taking the drug (hazard ratio [HR] 2.09, confidence interval [CI] 1.29 to 3.39).

There was, however, no difference in risk of nursing home placement for any of the four groups during the following three years. Starting memantine – either alone or in combination – was found to have no effect on risk of nursing home placement.

How did the researchers interpret the results?

The researchers concluded by saying that, 'Withdrawal of donepezil in patients with moderate to severe Alzheimer's disease increased the risk of nursing home placement during 12 months of treatment, but made no difference during the following three years of follow-up.

'Decisions to stop or continue donepezil treatment should be informed by potential risks of withdrawal, even if the perceived benefits of continued treatment are not clear.'

Conclusion

This randomised controlled trial assessed the impact of continuing or discontinuing the Alzheimer's drug donepezil on the chances of nursing home admission in people with moderate to severe Alzheimer's.

The study examined discontinuing or continuing donepezil, either alone or in combination with memantine, or switching to memantine alone. Memantine is currently licensed for the treatment of moderate to severe Alzheimer's, while donepezil is only licensed for mild to moderate forms of the disease.

In this trial, people had already been taking donepezil for three to six months or more. These drugs are only given by specialists, and the continuation or discontinuation of the drug is usually decided on an individual basis, depending on a person's response and its effects on cognitive function.

The results of this study showed discontinuing donepezil was associated with an increased chance of participants being placed in a nursing home in the first year of not taking the drug, compared with those who continued to take it.

Meanwhile, starting memantine had no effect. There was, however, no significant difference between these groups in the three years after the drugs had been stopped.

Although randomised controlled trials are the best study design to look at whether a treatment works or not, it is difficult to draw firm conclusions from the results of this study alone.

The study has primarily examined the effects of continued donepezil treatment on whether someone is placed in a nursing home, not on cognitive function. We do not know donepezil reduced Alzheimer's symptoms and this was directly responsible for helping the person remain independent in their own home.

The researchers also have not measured any side effects in individuals who continued to take this drug, so we can't assess the impact on their quality of life.

It could be the case that some people would actually be happier in a nursing home. It would be presumptuous to assume going into a nursing home automatically represented a failure in treatment.

Although there are currently no drugs that can cure Alzheimer's disease, research like this is important as it could prove the benefits of early treatment, which may reduce the severity of symptoms and slow the progression of the disease.

If you or anyone you know has experienced the following symptoms on more than a few occasions, it is important to seek medical help:

- forgetting recent conversations or events
- forgetting the names of places and objects
- repeating yourself regularly, such as asking the same question several times
- showing poor judgement or finding it harder to make decisions
- becoming unwilling to try out new things or adapt to change.

Behind the headlines

http://www.nhs.uk/news/2015/10October/Pages/Cheap-Alzheimers-drug-may-help-keep-people-out-of-care-homes.aspx

Links to the headlines

Six pence drug could keep Alzheimer's patients out of care homes. *The Daily Telegraph*, October 27 2015

Dementia drug 'keeps patients out of nursing homes'. BBC News, October 27 2015

Alzheimer's drug may keep late-stage sufferers out of nursing homes. *The Guardian*, October 27 2015

6p-a-day drug saves dementia sufferers from going into care: Patients taking treatment found to be twice as likely to still live in their home a year later. *Daily Mail*, October 27 2015

Thousands of Alzheimer's sufferers could remain at home with £21 drug. *The Times*, October 27 2015

Links to the science

Howard, R., McShane, R., Lindesay, J., et al. Nursing home placement in the Donepezil and Memantine in Moderate to Severe Alzheimer's Disease (DOMINO-AD) trial: secondary and post-hoc analyses. *The Lancet Neurology*. [Published online October 26 2015]

Part B

SECTION 2: SOCIAL CARE RESEARCH

Article 2: Social care research: Cheap Alzheimer's drug 'may help keep people out of care homes'

Provide a list of the secondary sources you have used in addition to **Article 2**.

> Refer to the list of secondary sources you have prepared, using the same recognised referencing system (e.g. Harvard) you used in Part A, and list them here. When giving research sources:
> - list them in alphabetical order. If two references start with the same letter, list them in date order with the most recent date first
> - where an acronym is used, cite the full name and the acronym in brackets the first time it is used. You can then just use the acronym, e.g. Health and Social Care Information Centre (HSCIC).
>
> As a guide, spend no more than 10 minutes listing your secondary sources, prepared in your Part A notes.

1 What different research methods are referred to in this article and other research pieces you have researched about this issue?

In your answer you should include:

(a) how different methods of research have been used to find ways that may keep people with Alzheimer's out of care homes

(b) how valid the conclusions drawn from these methods are.

15 marks

As a guide, spend about **40 minutes** answering Question 1.

In your answer, show your understanding of research methods and the validity and reliability of results of the research. For example:
- explain the research methods and show your understanding of data usage
- support your evaluative judgements on suitability
- show your understanding of other research methods used to explore the issue
- support your conclusions on reliability, showing an understanding of the concept in the context of the methods used.

....

....

....

....

....

....

....

....

....

....

....

....

....

....

....

....

....

....

....

....

....

....

....

....

....

....

....

....

....

....

....

....

....

....

....

....

....

....

Links Look at pages 172–176 of the Revision Guide to revise research methods and pages 209–211 to revise approaches to Question 1.

Total for Question 1 = 15 marks

2 Why is research into the ways that may keep people out of care homes important for individuals?

In your answer you should include how far your own secondary research into this issue supports the conclusions drawn in the article.

15 marks

As a guide, spend about **40 minutes** answering Question 2.

In your answer, show your understanding of the relationship between your own secondary research and the provided article, and how this relationship reinforces the importance of the issue. For example:
- analyse the issue, leading to conclusions about the issue's importance
- provide relevant examples of effects on individuals, supported by research findings
- explain the relationship between your secondary research findings and the issue in the article
- show your understanding of the relationship between the two.

....

....

....

....

....

....

....

....

....

....

....

....

....

....

....

....

....

....

....

....

....

....

....

....

....

....

....

....

....

....

....

....

....

....

....

....

....

....

....

....

....

....

....

Links Look at page 169 of the Revision Guide to revise issues in health and social care, page 192 for relationships between sources and pages 212–213 for approaches to Question 2.

Total for Question 2 = 15 marks

3 You are planning to carry out further research into ways that may help keep people out of care homes. What will you need to consider when planning this research?

In your answer you should refer to the article and your own secondary research.

15 marks

As a guide, spend about **40 minutes** answering Question 3.

In your answer, show your understanding of planning and ethical considerations for further research, supporting any judgements made. For example:
- suggest research methods that could be used to continue investigation/exploration into the issue and give your reasons why
- show your understanding of why the methods chosen are effective and suitable, and justify the choices
- show your analysis skills
- cover the planning considerations, ethical issues and necessary research skills required to explore the issue, showing your understanding of the practical problems involved in conducting research.

....
....
....
....
....
....
....
....
....
....
....
....
....
....
....
....
....
....
....
....
....
....

....

....

....

....

....

....

....

....

....

....

....

....

....

....

....

....

....

Links Look at pages 170–176 of the Revision Guide to revise planning research, pages 177–182 for ethical considerations, page 202 for identifying future research and pages 214–216 for approaches to Question 3.

Total for Question 3 = 15 marks

4 How can this research help social care professionals to support people with Alzheimer's to stay out of care homes?

In your answer you should refer to the article and your own secondary research.

20 marks

As a guide, spend about **50 minutes** answering Question 4.

In your answer, show your understanding of research implications for future provision and/or practice.
For example:
- analyse and explain the implications of the research for provision/practice in the sector in a clear, orderly way
- show your understanding of the implications of the issue in the context of the article and wider research
- justify your recommendations for change
- give supported reasons for any implications.

....

....

....

....

....

....

....

....

....

> **Links** Look at pages 200 and 201 of the Revision Guide to revise implications of research for practice and for the provision of services, and pages 217–218 to revise approaches to Question 4.

Total for Question 4 = 20 marks

END OF REVISION TASK

TOTAL FOR REVISION TASK = 65 marks

Answers

Unit 1: Human Lifespan Development

Revision paper 1 (guided)
(pages 2–14)

1 Example answer:
  1 Anna will be able to walk and climb on low furniture because she will have developed the muscles in her back and legs.
  2 Anna will be able to hold a crayon in a palmar grasp because she has developed control in the small muscles of her hands and fingers.

2 Emotional development.

3 Example answer:
According to Piaget's stages of development, at 8 years old Oscar is in the concrete operations stage. He will still need concrete apparatus such as counters to help him to work out problems. Oscar will now be able to conserve. This means that he can think logically and realise that amounts stay the same when they are moved or put into different-shaped containers. Piaget believed that, until the age of 7 children are egocentric. This means that until recently Oscar will have believed that others see and feel things in the same way as he does. Now that Oscar is 8, he will be able to understand things from the perspective of other people.

4 Example content may include:
  • stress increases the risk of disease, such as heart disease, and cancers
  • grief can mean Jan will care less about his diet and may eat unhealthily
  • lack of nutrients leads to ill health
  • a predisposition to disease, e.g. heart disease and cancers, can be activated by stress
  • research by Holmes and Rahe shows a correlation between stress and ill health.

5 Example answer:
Bowlby concluded that early attachment is important as it forms a model for all other attachments. Having a strong attachment with Jan helps Anna to feel emotionally secure, which will help her to cope emotionally at the nursery. According to Schaffer and Emerson's stages of attachment, after the age of 9 months children will start to develop attachments to others. Anna may be upset when Jan first leaves, but at her age she is likely to be able to form a positive attachment to her main carer at the nursery.

6 Example content may include:
  • **Emotional:**
    ◦ Improved self-image and higher self-esteem.
    ◦ Improved sleep patterns.
    ◦ Increased confidence.
    ◦ Reduced stress and anxiety.
    ◦ More independence.
  • **Social:**
    ◦ Meeting new people at work.
    ◦ More money to go out and socialise.
  • **Intellectual:**
    ◦ Stimulated because having to make decisions and judgements in his job.
  • **Physical:**
    ◦ More active because he is going to work.
    ◦ More money for leisure activities.
    ◦ Improvements in physical and mental health.
  • **Effects on children:**
    ◦ Will feel more secure if Jan is not showing anxiety.
    ◦ Improved diet if more financially secure.
    ◦ May feel more anxious or less secure because Jan will not be at home as much.

7 Example answer:
Bullying is likely to make Oscar feel isolated. This will impact on his self-image and lower his self-esteem. He could become frightened and anxious, which can lead to headaches and sleeping difficulties. If bullying continues, it can have more serious effects on emotional development, leading to depression or other mental health problems. In the long term, bullying could result in Oscar self-harming or even attempting or committing suicide.

8 Example answer:
The health visitor will measure Anna's height and weight and check these against centiles that show the average for girls of Anna's age. He or she will plot this on a chart. If Anna is growing more slowly or quickly than expected, the health visitor will consider referring her to a paediatrician.
Maturation theory was developed by observing the abilities and skills of large numbers of children at different ages. The information was used to determine norms called milestones that children will reach at a given age. The health visitor can apply them when she or he observes and assesses development.
The health visitor can use the information from the assessments to identify developmental delay.
Using information that shows the expected norms for children is important because it will enable the health visitor to plan support to help Anna to reach her milestones.

9 Example answer:
A large number of lorries would substantially increase pollution in the atmosphere near the family home. Pollution can have a serious impact on the respiratory system, causing breathing difficulties, particularly in young children such as Oscar and Anna.
Nitrogen oxides and soot particles in diesel fuel can also cause heart disease and lung damage or affect the functions of the brain.
Pollution can worsen or complicate existing conditions such as asthma, or cause the onset of diseases such as cancer if Jan or either of the children has a predisposition. The family may be less likely to go outside to play because of the noise or to go for walks, which will affect their mental wellbeing and quality of life.

10 Example answer:
  1 Pharmacy
  2 Counselling services
  3 Welfare benefits

11 Example answer:
In later adulthood, as a normal part of ageing, individuals will usually notice a decline in the functions of their body. Cardiovascular disease becomes more common because of raised cholesterol or high blood pressure. Other diseases that are linked to ageing are Parkinson's disease (caused by degeneration of nervous tissue), osteoarthritis, degeneration of the sense organs and dementia.
Poor lifestyle choices are likely to increase the rate of decline and cause the onset of disease.
A healthy lifestyle is important because feeling physically healthy will improve Gita's mental wellbeing. Maintaining a healthy weight through diet and exercise could help her mobility. Diet is more important in ageing because of the decline in absorption of nutrients.
Although changes in lifestyle choices will not prevent some decline in ageing, they can help to keep people healthier for longer.
A healthy lifestyle is particularly important for Gita at her life stage because it can help her to remain active and healthy for longer by slowing the impact of ageing.

12 Example answer:

1 An ageing population means a higher demand on health and social care services. This may impact on the availability of services or increase waiting times for the whole population.

2 An ageing population means an increase in the ratio of retired people to working people. This means higher numbers of retirees claiming state pensions and welfare compared with working people. This results in fewer people paying taxes to pay for pensions and other welfare costs, such as winter fuel payments.

13 Example content may include:

Genetic factors:
- Both Gita and her daughter suffered with breast cancer.
- Family history of mental health problems.

Environmental factors:
- Life events causing stress, e.g. divorce and death of daughter.

Lifestyle factors:
- Increased likelihood of illness due to:
  ○ poor diet
  ○ lack of exercise
  ○ smoking
  ○ sleeping tablets.

Conclusion:
- The genetic risks of physical and mental illness could have been increased by stress.
- Issues are exacerbated by financial difficulties.
- The onset of mental health problems is explained by the stress–diathesis model.
- Increased risks to health are explained by the Holmes-Rahe social adjustment scale.

Revision paper 2 (pages 15–25)

1 Example answer:

At 4 years old Shona will be able to manipulate small objects with her fingers and have good hand–eye coordination. This means that she will be able to do up and undo her buttons to dress and undress without help. Shona will be able to feed herself because she will be skilful when she uses a spoon and fork and will be beginning to use a knife.

Shona will be able to take part in the play activities with other children because she can hold and control a pencil and paintbrush using a tripod grasp. She will be able to take part in craft activities because she can cut out with scissors and thread small beads. Shona can manipulate objects, so she will be able to build towers with construction blocks and play games such as jigsaws.

2 Example answer:

1 Truancy.
2 Smoking.
3 Being disrespectful.

3 Example answer:

1 If Arlene continues to drink alcohol it will expose the unborn baby to alcohol, which can cause premature birth, low birth weight or even stillbirth. Excessive alcohol use may lead to foetal alcohol syndrome in the baby, which can result in learning disability, distinctive facial characteristics and heart or kidney defects.

2 Smoking can reduce the amount of oxygen that gets to the baby, and the red blood cells will carry chemicals from cigarettes through the umbilical cord. This can cause low birth weight and babies may be born with heart conditions.

4 Example content may include:

Bandura's social learning theory:
- Children learn from watching others.
- They imitate observed behaviour when they have the opportunity.
- They are more likely to copy if they see the model getting satisfaction or good feedback.
- A negative outcome discourages imitation of the behaviour.
- A positive outcome encourages imitation of the behaviour.

- It is important to be a good role model because children:
  ○ learn from positive behaviour
  ○ copy negative behaviour
  ○ can be motivated to imitate and repeat positive behaviour.
- Social learning theory ignores theories that behaviours/ responses may be influenced by genetic inheritance (nature and not nurture).
- Bandura's theory does not explain why children sometimes display behaviour that is not learned from a role model.

5 Example content may include:

Piaget's stages of cognitive development:
- Children are in the pre-operational stage from 2–7 years old.
- Children need to play an active role in their own learning.
- Free play enables children to explore.
- Children need to build their experiences of the world by exploring materials.
- Children use their senses to learn about the environment.
- Children need to explore their environment to develop schemas.
- Children assimilate new information as they explore their environment.
- Active learning helps children to construct new schemas.
- Children need to use symbols as a form of representation in their imaginative play.
- Children need opportunities to use symbolic behaviour in pretend play.

Criticism:
- If adults lead children's play they can support children to move to the next stage of learning.

6 Example answer:

When Kai begins puberty his voice will gradually change and begin to deepen, which is referred to as the voice 'breaking'. He will notice that he is growing more quickly and may experience a growth spurt over a short period of time. He will grow pubic and underarm hair. Kai will also notice changes relating to his sexual and reproductive organs, which were present when he was born but will mature during puberty with the release of hormones. His prostate gland will begin to produce secretions. His penis and testes will both enlarge and he will begin to produce sperm.

7 Example answer:

1 Mike will have grown to his full height and strength, so will have reached the peak of his physical fitness.

2 At Mike's life stage he is likely to be starting or in the early period of employment, which will give him independence leading to positive self-esteem.

8 Example answer:

Emotionally, Arlene may experience anxiety and stress from the break up. This can significantly affect her self-image and lead to negative self-esteem. She may feel less secure and upset for the children because their father is no longer there for them. Alternatively, if the partnership was difficult, Arlene could feel relieved and enjoy her independence. Arlene may find that her social circle changes as she is no longer part of a couple. It may also be more difficult to get out to socialise because she is now the children's only carer.

9 Example content may include:

Sofia is in the middle adulthood, life stage, which may involve changes such as:
- Children are now independent.
- Sofia may have personal independence, leading to increased socialisation.
- She may be financially secure, giving her more independence and choice, and be affected positively and negatively by economic factors.
- Sofia may notice a change in her physical ability and appearance:
  ○ greying hair
  ○ loss of muscle tone, strength and stamina
  ○ her body shape may change with an increase in, or loss of, weight.

- Sofia may feel down because she is no longer fertile as menstruation ends.
- She is likely to experience menopause at her life stage. Oestrogen production will decrease, causing:
  - hot flushes
  - vaginal dryness
  - mood swings
  - reduced libido
  - dry hair and skin.

10 Line a

11 Example content may include:

Relating to activity theory:
- Mary continued to need activity and social interaction for her wellbeing.
- She continued to involve herself in the local community and her church.
- She was able to meet her psychological needs by volunteering.
- She met her social needs through her involvement with the church and charity shop.
- Although she had some decline in health, she adjusted and remained active.
- She continued to be independent and take care of her appearance.

Relating to social disengagement theory:
- People naturally withdraw from social contact in older age.
- Other people may have withdrawn from Mary.
- Sofia may have begun to expect less from Mary, so she lost confidence and self-esteem.
- Mary has been forced to become dependent.

Conclusion:
- Mary may have continued to be intellectually and physically active if she had not undergone trauma.
- Other factors may have affected Mary's development, such as dementia.

12 Example answer:

Older people are more at risk of falls because their strength and mobility are likely to deteriorate. Illnesses that affect the brain, such as degeneration of the nervous tissue or Alzheimer's, are more common in older people and these can cause disorientation, confusion and slow reaction time. With ageing, hypotension can cause blood pressure to drop, which can cause older people to lose their balance when getting up quickly. Sensory problems also become more common in later life. Illness that affects the inner ear may cause dizziness, and stairs become an increasing hazard with deterioration of sight.

13 Example content may include:
- The fall has restricted Mary's mobility.
- Her independence has been lost because of the fall, which will affect her self-esteem.
- Mary may get anxious about her future because she is less active.
- Lack of activity may lead to other illness common in ageing, such as heart disease.
- Poor diet may lead to weaker muscles, bones and increased risk of infection.
- Mary is likely to worry about becoming totally dependent on others.
- She might worry about her death.
- She may have lost confidence in carrying out tasks.
- The fall has led to her becoming isolated.
- She is likely to feel angry towards others because of her situation.
- She may be grieving for her lost life when she could take an active role.
- The fall could have caused depression, which has resulted in her lack of interest in personal hygiene.

Unit 2: Working in Health and Social Care

Revision paper 1 (guided)

Section A: Scenario 1: Ill health (pages 27–30)

1 (a) Example answer:
  1 Whether Carlos is attempting to disguise his weight loss.
  2 Whether Carlos wants to keep control of personal information such as weight loss so does not want to be weighed.

(b) Example answer:
  1 The staff might explain to Carlos about eating disorders, the type of disorder he has and the effects which it could have on him, such as psychological, emotional and physical effects.
  2 The staff might ask Carlos questions about his lifestyle, such as details of his diet and whether he is worried about his attitude to food.

(c) Answer content may include:
- One of the main barriers to accessing health and social care services is the unwillingness of people to seek help when they need it. This can be the case with people who have mental ill health, which is sometimes the cause of eating disorders.
- In the case of Carlos, a reason might be his sexual preferences. People may prefer not to disclose their sexuality.
- A further reason might be that people cannot afford it. For example, the cost of travel or of the service itself may be too much.
- A reason people might not access social care services is because they will have to pay for them. For example, older people may need residential care but don't want to use their savings to pay for their care.
- In conclusion, some of the main reasons why people do not access the health and social care services they need might be related to mental health, being worried about something (e.g. reluctant to disclose sexuality) or financial concerns.
- Others may not access services because of cultural reasons (e.g. worried about taking their clothes off), geographical reasons (e.g. difficulty in reaching services) or lack of knowledge (e.g. because they don't know about the services available).

(d) Answer content may include:
- It is a priority that Carlos continues his recovery and maintains good mental and physical health. Health and social care staff might provide him with a healthy eating plan that is monitored by members of his family and by the support staff carrying out regular checks during future appointments. The staff also need to put in place measures which will prevent the likelihood of a relapse, so their proposals need to be agreed with Carlos to meet his needs and preferences.
- Carlos may feel that the most important need is to be able to tell his family that he is gay. The staff might help him to find ways to do this, for example, by providing him with counselling to help him understand and feel proud of who he is rather than worrying about what people might think.
- The counsellor might suggest that he tells the person he trusts most first of all. This would empower Carlos by leaving the decision to him.
- The staff might encourage Carlos to look at the support which is available online to help him and this would enable him to reach decisions in his own time.
- Online help could also help him to maintain his privacy.
- In conclusion, the staff should ensure that any communications with Carlos reflect key care values

which ensure that he is empowered and respected, and his rights are protected. Carlos should retain his dignity, and if he decides that he does not wish to disclose information about his sexuality, then his wish for confidentiality must be respected.

Section B: Scenario 2: Learning disability (pages 31–34)

2 (a) Example answer:
1 Help with feeding
2 Help with mobility.

(b) Example answer:
1 The carers help family members to manage Salome when she exhibits challenging behaviour. They could show Salome's family some strategies which are designed to calm her down in these situations.
2 The carers might also show family members ways to prevent Salome physically harming herself. These ways could include how to put Salome's clothes on without harming her or others, if Salome struggles when being dressed.

(c) Answer content may include:
- Health and social care workers who support people with profound learning disabilities need skills which enable them to respond to, and manage, complex needs. As Salome has a range of other physical disabilities and mental ill health, staff need to be able to support these conditions and minimise their effects on Salome.
- Health and social care workers also need to try to understand which symptoms and behaviours are the result of a learning disability and which are not. One way of doing this is to spend time with the person to understand their needs, so they know how to use their skills and experience to meet these needs, or where they might need further training or continuing professional development (CPD).
- Staff also need to have communication skills that are effective when working with people who have mild or profound learning disabilities. They need to be able to recognise and interpret the meanings of certain behaviours and reactions, especially when they are challenging. They do this by staying open-minded about the people they support and being willing to learn about their needs and preferences. Staff who support people with learning disabilities may also try to display empathy with their clients.
- In conclusion, if support is given as explained above, it means that people such as Salome who have learning disabilities would have support that is tailored to specific needs. Salome would have choice and control over the things that are important to her. Salome's dignity would also be maintained while meeting her day-to-day needs and she and her family would be treated with respect.

(d) Answer content may include:
- Firstly, the most effective way to help people with a learning disability to communicate is through partnership working, by involving a range of people and organisations. These might include family members, frontline staff, advocates, service managers and people who plan and commission services.
- To help a person with learning disabilities, family members, frontline staff and advocates should not make assumptions about their needs and preferences. Making assumptions could limit the person's opportunities.
- They should encourage communication of needs and preferences using a variety of methods, and specially trained staff will be able to communicate them to family members who help with the person's care.
- One way that people with a learning disability can communicate their needs and preferences is by learning new skills. This would enable them to do something for themselves and so to communicate their own wishes. While Salome would find this very difficult, there are some basic skills, such as being able to wash her hands, that she could do from time to time. This could help her start to manage her frustration, benefit her mental health, and help introduce positive communication, resulting in less frequent challenging behaviour.
- In conclusion, by helping people such as Salome to communicate their needs and preferences through learning new skills such as practical hand-washing or using alternative methods of communication such as gestures or signs, they can lead more meaningful lives.

Section C: Scenario 3: Physical/sensory disabilities (pages 35–38)

3 (a) Example answer:
1 Accident and emergency nurse.
2 Healthcare assistant.

(b) Example answers:
1 A nurse would prepare a care plan for Lars. This would be likely to recommend that he has physiotherapy to help him build his muscle strength.
2 An occupational therapist might help Lars with adaptations to his home. Recommendations might include lowering work surfaces in the kitchen so that Lars can easily reach them from his wheelchair.

(c) Answer content may include:
Hospitals are inspected by staff from external agencies, such as the Care Quality Commission (CQC) in England.
- When hospitals are inspected, the inspectors ask people who use the services provided by the hospital for their views, to find out whether they are satisfied with the ways they have been treated. This enables the inspectors to make a judgement about the quality of care which is being provided.
- Inspectors also observe staff at the hospital providing care for patients.
- They look at the patient records and individual care plans and check whether they meet the needs and preferences of the patients.
- In conclusion, the findings of the inspection are published by the CQC and these can be read by people who want to know about the quality of the services provided. As a result of the inspection, the hospital and individuals might need to respond to findings and put improvement action plans in place. These might affect working practices and staff training, so that services are improved.

(d) Answer content may include:
- People like Lars will need help to deal with their diagnosis. The surgeon will tell Lars the outcome of the accident, explain what treatment is available, how likely it is to be successful, what he is likely to be able to do when he has recovered, and the support that will be put in place, such as physiotherapists, occupational therapists and counsellors.
- As part of coming to terms with a physical disability, the person will need to tell their family and friends, who will also have to come to terms with what has happened.
- Family and friends will also help someone like Lars come to terms with his condition. For example, they might support him in adjusting to these unexpected life events while he is still in hospital, and then with the transition back home. They might help Lars to complete exercises set by the physiotherapist or support the occupational therapist in helping Lars to adapt his home and manage daily tasks.
- The diagnosis of physical disability might also affect a person's mental health. If so, psychological services, such as counselling, could be used. For example, although Lars is very active after his accident, he might

also experience post-traumatic stress disorder or other forms of anxiety. This might not affect him straight away, but it could be a long-term effect, and a counsellor could suggest strategies to help Lars deal with his anxiety.

- People like Lars might also use the services of sports therapists who are trained to help people return to sports after an accident. For example, archery might be recommended to build his upper body strength.
- Returning to work and feeling confident using his wheelchair, as well as having accessible public transport and an accessible office environment, will also help Lars come to terms with his condition. If this goes well, it will help to increase his independence, although there may be times when health and social care may be needed to help Lars overcome any difficulties.
- In conclusion, health and social care workers play key roles in helping people to come to terms with and recover from illness and accidents. These roles enable people like Lars to remain independent, which is a key care value and aim of the services provided.

Section D: Scenario 4: Age-related needs (pages 39–42)

4 (a) Example answer:
1   He will be in a familiar environment – a place he knows and recognises so he will know where everything is, as he can't see very well.
2   He will be with his family.
   (b) Example answer:
1   The nurse will give Hal his medication. This will help him to manage the impact of his pain and have the best possible quality of life.
2   The nurse will talk to Hal about the impact on his mental health of being diagnosed with an incurable or terminal illness. Because Hal has to manage his pain, this is likely to affect his mental wellbeing.
   (c) Answer content may include:
- Health and social care services are provided in different settings in order to meet the widest range of needs.
- Hospice care can be delivered in different settings, including in people's homes and residential care settings, but other types of health and social care can only be delivered in specific settings. For example, operations (such as the removal of brain tumours) can only be carried out in hospitals where the facilities and staff are in place.
- Because Hal prefers to remain in his own home, the Marie Curie nurse care provides care there.
- For people like Hal, it is important that services are provided in different settings because this is the most effective way to meet his needs.
- Finally, providing services in different settings can be cost effective. Spending can be focused on meeting different needs, for example by providing specialist equipment in a highly resourced surgical unit alongside supported care in a person's home.
   (d) Answer content may include:
- Marie Curie nurses are trained to provide high standards of care for people in their own homes. They are expected to maintain a professional approach, underpinned by the qualifications which they must have to become specialist nurses.
- Another responsibility of health care staff (such as Marie Curie nurses) is to report any changes in their patient's condition. When Hal's condition deteriorates, the Marie Curie nurse must report this to the district nurse who prepared Hal's care plan. This is part of his or her professional duty as a nurse.
- One further aspect of palliative care is to support patients to live as actively as possible until they die.

Other healthcare staff might be involved to help the patient with psychological, social and spiritual support.
- Providing multidisciplinary support is a key aspect of meeting the patient's needs most effectively and is embedded in the responsibilities of healthcare staff who provide end-of-life care.
- Some benefits of end-of-life care at home include familiarity of surroundings and being with family. Some benefits of being cared for in a hospice include constant specialist care and potential respite for the family.
- Finally, healthcare workers also have responsibilities to support people who are related to the patient.
- The management of pain and other symptoms is paramount in palliative care, which aims to affirm life and regards dying as a normal process.

Revision paper 2

Section A: Scenario 1: Ill health (pages 43–45)

1 (a) Example answers:
1   Obstetrician.
2   Nurse.
   (b) Example answers:
1   They might recommend a healthy diet for Marquette during her pregnancy. This would be designed so that both Marquette and her unborn child get the right nutrients.
2   They could help Marquette to take regular exercise. They would tell her to avoid certain types of exercise, such as contact sports, where there is a risk of physical injury.
   (c) Answer content may include:
- Midwives are trained to support mothers during pregnancy, childbirth and the first 28 days of a baby's life.
- After the baby has been born, midwives provide postnatal care, supporting the mother, baby and wider family. This could include giving advice on breastfeeding, washing and getting the newborn baby to sleep.
- Another part of the role of the midwife is to help the mother to recover from the birth. If the mother experiences postnatal depression, the midwife will recommend available treatments and ways of dealing with it.
- The midwife will prepare and review patient care plans. This could mean that he or she has to arrange and/or provide parenting and health education.
- The midwife can also liaise with other agencies to ensure continuity of care.
- Marquette's baby was born healthy, but if this had not been the case, the midwife would provide support and advice following miscarriage, termination or neonatal death.
   (d) Answer content may include:
- People who work in health and social care settings have to follow the regulations set down by the professional bodies which regulate services in their sector. Examples of professional bodies are the Nursing and Midwifery Council, the Royal College of Nursing and the General Medical Council (which regulates the work of doctors).
- Workers are accountable because they must follow codes of professional conduct. For example, the code of conduct for midwives like Gregory means that they have to put a mother-to-be like Marquette at the heart of the care provided for her. This shows that he is following one of the key principles of the code, which is to prioritise people.
- Healthcare workers must ensure that they are fit to practise. For example, nurses must follow the Royal

College of Nursing requirement that they have to complete 450 hours of practice every three years in order to keep their professional status as a nurse. This is called revalidation and shows they are accountable to a professional body.

- Healthcare workers are also accountable when they follow safeguarding regulations. One way that safeguarding is maintained is by ensuring that personal information about service users remains confidential and is only shared either with the service users' consent or with other professionals on a need-to-know basis.
- In conclusion, healthcare workers must be accountable to professional bodies because this is one way of showing service users that they can trust the people who support them with their health needs.

Section B: Scenario 2: Learning disability (pages 46–48)

2   (a) Example answer:
    1   Need: additional support with learning from a teaching assistant.
    2   Right: to be treated in the same ways as other learners.
    (b) Example answer:
    1   It promotes understanding of diversity. For example, anti-discrimination training can be used to explain the benefits of having people with learning disabilities working in health and social care settings.
    2   It helps to minimise conflict. Anti-discrimination training can help to clarify the needs of people with learning disabilities and how these needs can be met.
    (c) Answer content may include:
    - Organisations which provide health and social care services must ensure that employees understand how to implement codes of practice. This helps people like Imran know what to expect when using services such as those provided by the health visitors.
    - Organisations must ensure that all staff who work in health and social care settings should also carry out continuing professional development (CPD) to ensure that they know and understand changes in current best practice. As well as this, organisations must ensure that future employees meet national occupational standards. These are designed to ensure that high-quality services are provided.
    - Finally, organisations which provide health and social care services must ensure that their employees are safeguarded. One way they can do this is by posting notices in health and social care settings reminding service users that employees must not be targets of discrimination or any type of abuse, whether verbal or physical.
    (d) Answer content may include:
    - Firstly, people who work in health and social care settings, such as doctors and nurses, have access to information about the health and care needs of their patients. They must keep this information confidential.
    - This means that they must only share the information with other healthcare workers who need to know it or if they have been given permission by the patient to share the information.
    - They must follow legislation set out in the Data Protection Act 1998 (DPA). This legislation is supported by the codes of practice which are in place in every setting where health and social care services are provided. Codes of practice tell service users what they can expect from organisations.
    - Another aspect of maintaining confidentiality about clients is the recording, storing and retrieval of information. This is also covered by the DPA. Patients have the right to know if their information is stored electronically, and the information must be stored securely, for example by being password protected.

- Finally, it is important to recognise the role which care values play in maintaining confidentiality.
- It is the right of service users like Imran to request confidentiality. Regardless of requests for information from other learners, Imran's teachers must not disclose information about him unless, for example, he agreed to it. This respects his rights and protects his dignity.

Section C: Scenario 3: Physical/sensory disabilities (pages 49–51)

3   (a) Example answers:
    1   Numbness.
    2   Impaired vision.
    (b) Example answers:
    1   Voluntary organisations and charities provide online information which can be accessed from home. This enables people to find out how to cope with disabilities. For example, the Multiple Sclerosis Society offers advice about how to deal with numbness and impaired vision.
    2   Voluntary organisations and charities enable people to access disability benefits. They provide information about personal independence payments (PIPs) which go towards the costs of paying for any help which might be needed.
    (c) Answer content may include:
    - Firstly, care workers will carry out a risk assessment. In Fay's case, they will assess her home and identify any changes that need to be made so that she can live more easily with multiple sclerosis.
    - Another aspect of safety is to ensure that clients are safeguarded and protected from abuse. This is particularly important if the client is a child or is vulnerable.
    - In care settings, another way that safety is ensured is through illness prevention measures. This means that clean toilets, hand-washing facilities and safe drinking water must be available in order to minimise the likelihood of infections. This is very important in hospitals, for example, and is a key way to ensure patient safety.
    - Finally, in addition to the range of safety measures outlined, all accidents and incidents must be reported to the relevant person in charge so the situation can be dealt with appropriately and practice can be improved.
    (d) Answer content may include:
    - The first care priority is to help the person deal with the diagnosis.
    - With a serious, long-term condition, such as multiple sclerosis, there may be an impact on the person's mental wellbeing which must be taken into consideration when providing care and support.
    - As the scenario points out, it will also be a care priority to support other members of the person's family.
    - All care must reflect the individual's needs and preferences.
    - In Fay's case, her physical and sensory needs will probably be considered before her preferences but these should be acknowledged as far as possible when planning her care.
    - When taking into account her needs and preferences, care planning must enable Fay to access the health services she needs. This is another priority.
    - Fay might also need specialised equipment to help her carry out day-to-day routines and her care planning must ensure that she has access to this. An example might be a motorised wheelchair.
    - As the scenario points out, another priority must be respite care. Because her daughters are helping her, it is vital that all members of the family have access to respite.

- Finally, alongside the range of care outlined above, Fay might also be supported to access self-care programmes which will help her to remain independent.

Section D: Scenario 4: Age-related needs (pages 52–54)

4 (a) Example answers:
1 Mental health nurse.
2 Healthcare assistant (HCA).

(b) Example answers:
1 When he was admitted to the nursing home, members of Drake's family could give care staff information about what he prefers to eat and drink. They could tell them that Drake cannot eat or drink without help.
2 They could tell care staff what causes Drake to become agitated and how they find it best to calm Drake down.

(c) Answer content may include:
- Health and social care workers, such as mental health nurses who specialise in dementia, are trained to provide practical and psychological support to family members. They are honest with children about illnesses in adults like Drake, so the children know what to expect.
- They are trained to spot when children are affected by the news and the ways that their behaviour can change. For example, Drake's young relatives might exhibit grief and sadness when they hear about his illness. The health and social care worker or dementia specialist nurse would encourage them to express their feelings.
- They would also support children who might feel confused and angry because they no longer get the same level of attention from Drake or from their parents. This might involve informal discussions as a family group with health and social care workers, or some counselling if appropriate.
- The specialist nurse might also suggest ways that the children could help Drake so they feel included and involved in his care, and help them to feel loved and wanted.
- Finally, in addition to the range of approaches detailed above, they would help the children to understand that their support for Drake won't cure his dementia but that it will help him.

(d) Answer content may include:
- Because Drake is unable to make any decisions for himself, other people, including members of his family, may make some of them for him. This is one aspect of advocacy.
- Drake's family believe that they have his best interests at heart and that they know and understand his needs and preferences based on their experience of living with him and, for those reasons, they are his advocates.
- Advocacy is important because it enables people like Drake who cannot make their own decisions to access the information and services they need. It defends and promotes their rights. It also ensures that their views and concerns are taken seriously.
- Another issue which affects the ways that care is provided for people like Drake is the experience and knowledge of health professionals such as mental health nurses, particularly those who specialise in dementia. They will assess Drake's needs. For example, the nurse will balance his medication and recommend the types of care that he needs.
- Nurses must also have excellent communication skills in order to take into account the needs of Drake's family as well as his own.
- Finally, legislation such as the Mental Capacity Act 2005, the Mental Health Act 1983 (amended 2007) and power of attorney requirements protects and supports people like Drake. For example, the Mental Capacity Act covers decisions relating to personal care, including what to wear and what to eat.

- These ways of responding to the range of issues involved in providing care for people like Drake, who cannot make decisions for themselves, help to ensure that they are protected and supported.

Unit 3: Anatomy and Physiology for Health and Social Care

Revision paper 1 (guided)

Questions 1–3: The lungs (pages 56–59)

1 (a) C
(b) B = bronchus, D = alveoli, F = pleura.
(c) B

2 (a) Answer content may include:
- The mucus is very thick, so is difficult to cough up. This means that the lungs become clogged with mucus. Therefore, lung function is reduced to less than 20% of that of a person with fully functioning lungs and the lungs can easily become infected.
- Over the years, the lungs become increasingly damaged due to the coughing and physiotherapy to get rid of the mucus, so work even less effectively, leading to more life-threatening respiratory problems, such as pneumonia.

(b) Example answer:
The term *genetic disorder* means a disorder or disability that occurs as a result of inheriting a gene or chromosome abnormality.

3 (a) Example answer:
The volume of air in the person's lungs has increased, so the person must have been asked to take a deep breath. This means that the air in the lungs at point A will contain a high level of oxygen and a low level of carbon dioxide.

(b) A = Tidal, B = Inspiratory

Questions 4–6: The digestive system (pages 60–63)

4 A = Pancreas, B = Colon

5 (a) D
(b) Answer content may include:
Simple epithelial cells are found in areas which are not subject to abrasion, such as the villi, and where secretion of mucus is needed to trap unwanted particles and act as a lubricant to move them on.
Compound epithelial cells are found in areas which are subject to abrasion, such as the lining of the oesophagus, in layers which protect both deeper structures and multiple layers of cells. Older cells are pushed to the surface and flattened to form a protective layer.

6 (a) Example answer:
Gastric juices and stomach acid in the stomach destroy a small area of mucous membrane, producing an open sore. Bacterial action on this open sore can lead to these symptoms and even bleeding.

(b) $7.0 \div 2.2 = 3.2$ times or 320%

(c) Example answer:
The bar chart shows that there is a correlation between the use of some prescription drugs and an increased probability of developing ulcer complications. However, the data doesn't tell us anything about other possible factors that might contribute towards the development of ulcers, such as infection or lifestyle choices, and it also shows that age is a factor. Overall, the data does suggest that taking certain prescription drugs, such as NSAIDs and anticoagulants, does cause ulcer complications.

Question 7: Energy and homeostasis (page 64)

7 (a) Energy can be neither created nor destroyed.
(b) Sweat gland.
Arterioles in skin.

(c) Example answer:
- Body temperature rises.
- Thermal receptors in skin and around internal organs are stimulated.
- Behaviour is altered by (for example) removing clothes, a stretched out posture, drinking cool drinks.
- Body temperature decreases.

Questions 8–11: The skeletal system (pages 65–68)

8 (a) Example answer:
Up to age group '45 to 64': As babies and children develop and grow, their bones become harder and are more likely to break when they fall. As they become young people and adults, they take up more varied physical activities and start working, so are more likely to break bones.
From age group 45 to 64 onwards: As people age, their bones become less dense and more brittle, so that even a minor accident can lead to a break. They are also more likely to develop disorders such as osteoporosis, which causes bones to be thinner and more susceptible to breaking. Excessive wear and tear, known as osteoarthritis, and again most often associated with older people, can lead the cartilage on the ends of bones to break up, causing pain and restricted mobility, leading to a greater risk of falls and breaks. Younger people may get this as a result of their occupation, such as dancers or builders, or lifestyle, but it worsens with age, so again contributes to the upward trend of more breaks with age.

(b) Vitamin D.

(c) Example answer:
The menopause is when women stop having periods and is a natural part of ageing. Women usually go through the menopause between 45 and 55 years of age, as their oestrogen levels drop. Osteoporosis in women is often associated with a decrease in oestrogen secretion in the years following the menopause and leads to more brittle bones, and so a greater likelihood of breaks. This is why the reverse in the trend only starts to appear in the 65 plus age group.

9 (a) The axial skeleton.
(b) The axial skeleton.

10 Example answer:
'Flexion' describes the action when the angle between two bones decreases, as in touching the shoulder with same arm.

11 (a) Answer content may include:
Cartilage is the smooth, translucent, cushioning substance that protects bone ends from friction during movement and acts as a shock absorber in joints. It enables a degree of flexibility.
Ligaments are strap-like strong elasticated bands that run from bone to bone across a joint. They are made of yellow, elastic fibres of protein and have a limited degree of stretch. Their function is partly to hold the joint together while allowing movement but also to prevent overstretching and movement outside the normal range of the joint.
Although both are important parts of the skeletal system in joints, their structure, functions and flexibility are all different.

(b) Answer content may include:
- It is important for the carer to be aware of the range of movements allowed by different types of joint to avoid injuring themselves, people working with them and the service user. The key joint actions that may be affected by overstretching include extension, abduction and adduction. This can lead to wear and tear on the joints.
- There is also a risk of overstretching, straining or even snapping tendons and ligaments if exerting a large force on them, when lifting a heavy person.
- There is the possibility of irritating joints and discs, which leads to inflammation, fluid build-up and constriction of blood vessels and nerves in the spine.
- Doing the same motion over and over again can lead to repetitive strain injuries in the joints, especially in the wrists, fingers, shoulders and elbows.

Questions 12–13: The lymphatic and immune systems (pages 69–70)

12 (a) Axillary lymph node = F; Lymphatics of the mammary gland = A

(b)

Organ	Function (A, B, C, D or E)
Lymph nodes	E
Thymus	D
Spleen	C
Tonsils	A
Appendix	B

(c) D or thymus.

13 (a) Example answer:
The swelling is caused by an excess of affected B lymphocytes (white blood cells). These multiply abnormally, collecting in a lymph node (also called lymph gland). This causes the lymphocytes to lose their ability to fight infection. Patients may then develop an infection, which leads to a raised temperature or fever.

(b) Example answer:
There are many types of leukaemia, which is cancer of the blood and affects white blood cells. The two main types affect lymphocytes, which are part of the lymphatic system and which mostly fight viral infections, and myeloid cells, which fight bacterial infections. People with leukaemia have repeated infections because their bodies no longer have the infection-fighting properties of healthy white blood cells, so their immune system is affected. Leukaemia therefore mainly affects the lymphatic and immune systems.

Questions 14–16: The female and male reproductive systems (pages 71–74)

14 (a) Oestrogen = A, LH = D

15 Answer content may include:
- Although the data from the first study shows that over half the girls had additional painful conditions and that older women with endometriosis had more of these than younger girls with the same condition (suggesting that endometriosis affects the whole body), it is not conclusive because there is not enough detail about the study.
- We are not told how many girls of a similar age who **do not** have endometriosis also have these painful conditions, so there is no control group to compare the findings with.
- In the second study, MRI identified 92.8% of cases of endometriosis in the bladder, which is a high percentage.
- However, it only detected it in 86.8% of cases in the pouch of Douglas, 132 of the 152 women. This means that, if this had been the only diagnosis method used, 20 women would have been undiagnosed. It becomes increasing unreliable when used for other body locations, the worst being the peritoneum, with only 70.4% (107 women out of 152) being successfully diagnosed.
- The conclusion that MRI detects endometriosis 'quite well' is, therefore, fair but vague and suggests that further work needs to be done to find other methods of detection. 'Quite well' means different things to different people.
- Again, there is not enough information given here, such as the relative size of the patch of cells looked at in each case. If the patches were smaller in certain parts of the body, this would affect the findings.
- MRI is useful when it successfully detects endometriosis but this study shows that, when it isn't detected, a second method is needed, in case the condition has been missed.
- Overall, the studies provided useful information but neither provided enough information to be conclusive.

16 (a) Dosage of 70–74.9 Gy: C
Dosage of 75–79.9 Gy: B
Dosage of more than 80 Gy: A
Dosage of less than 70 Gy: D
(b): 12 years.

Question 17: Human genetics (pages 75–76)

17 Answer content may include:
E's genotype is Ss because some of his children are unaffected and others are affected.

Both parents A and B must be Ss, so have one normal allele and one sickle cell disease allele. The gene for sickle cell disease must be recessive. To have sickle cell disease, a child must have two copies of the sickle cell disease allele.

Parents A and B can have children of genotypes SS (completely unaffected), Ss (carrier of sickle cell disease) and ss (has sickle cell disease) in the ratio of 1:2:1 as shown by the genetic diagram.

There is a 1 in 2 chance that any given child will have the sickle cell disease allele combined with a normal allele, so each of their children, including E, had a probability of 1 in 2 (50%) of having a genotype of Ss.

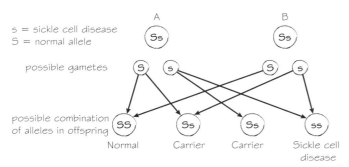

Revision paper 2

Questions 1–3: The skin (pages 77–80)

1 A = axon
B = myelin sheath

2 (a) C or adipose
(b) Example answer:
Areolar tissue is found in the dermis and adipose tissue in the subcutaneous layer. Areolar is flexible and offers support to the tissues it surrounds. Adipose helps to insulate the body against extreme temperature and acts as a shock absorber, so protects and stores energy.

3 (a) Example answer:
Each layer of healthy skin contains water, oils and fats. The skin acts as a barrier, keeping water in and preventing bacteria entering our bodies. People with eczema have dry skin, so the protective layer is not as effective. It does not produce as many fats and oils as normal skin and will be less able to retain water. Moisture is lost, allowing bacteria or other irritants to pass through more easily, so the skin is broken down more easily, becoming cracked.

(b) 7.9/1.2 = 6.6 times greater

(c) Example answer:
The bar chart shows that the relative prevalence of all three disorders is roughly consistent in all continents. However, the data doesn't tell us whether any of the children have more than one condition. What it does show is that children are more likely to develop one or more of these three conditions if they live on certain continents compared with others.

Question 4: Energy metabolism in the body (page 81)

4 (a) 'Metabolism' is the range of chemical processes that occur within a living organism in order to maintain life.

(b)

Aerobic respiration	Anaerobic respiration
Needs oxygen – yes or no? Yes	Needs oxygen – yes or no? No
Waste products: 1 Carbon dioxide 2 Water	Waste product: 1 Lactic acid
Large amount of energy from the breakdown of food	Small amount of energy from the breakdown of food

(c) Anaerobic

Questions 5–7: The renal system (pages 82–84)

5 (a) C
(b) A = Bladder
D = Liver
E = Ureters
(c) B

6 (a) Example answer:
In renal failure, the kidney cells undergo cellular death and are unable to filter waste and excess water from the blood, produce urine (necessary for washing away toxins) or maintain fluid and chemical balances. This leads to a build-up of water and other fluids in the body which cause swollen extremities.

(b) 'Progressive' means developing gradually, in stages.

7 (a) Example answer:
Diabetes causes injury to the small blood vessels in the body. When the blood vessels in the kidneys are injured, the kidneys cannot clean the blood properly, so water and waste materials build up in the body. This further increases the damage to the kidneys, until eventually they fail. Diabetes also causes nerve damage in the body, leading to difficulty emptying the bladder, which may lead to infection caused by the growth of bacteria in urine that has a high sugar level. The pressure from a persistently full bladder can injure the kidneys, as can infection that travels from the bladder to the kidneys.

(b) 1 Damage to the kidneys.
2 Kidney infection.

Questions 8–9: The muscular system (pages 85–86)

8 (a) Deltoids = A
Gluteus = F
(b)

Type of contraction	Change in length of contracting muscle	Example of use	Resulting action
Isometric (C)	Stays the same (E)	Carrying an object in front of you at same level or gripping a tennis racket	No movement in bones or joint(s) but muscle keeps bone(s) steady
Eccentric (A)	Lengthens (D)	Kicking a football	Control or deceleration of a movement
Concentric (F)	Shortens (B)	Bending the elbow from straight out to fully flexed	General movement of bones

9 (a) Example answer:
Muscular dystrophy is a group of genetic muscle disorders caused by a mutation in the genetic code (DNA). This affects the production of a muscle protein (dystrophin), so the muscle fibres gradually break down.

(b) Example answer:
Rickets is caused by a lack of vitamin D or calcium. Vitamin D comes mainly from exposing the skin to sunlight. Calcium is found in dairy products such as milk. Children generally now spend more time playing indoors on computer games or on social media and are often driven about by their parents, rather than walking, so they are not getting as much sunlight as many previous generations.

Questions 10–13: The digestive system (pages 87–89)

10 (a) Example answer:
Before the bolus: the inner circular muscle contracts, applying pressure to the bolus and the longitudinal muscle relaxes, pushing the bolus along.
After the bolus: the circular muscle relaxes and the longitudinal muscle contracts, applying pressure to hold the tube open to receive the bolus.

(b) The islets of Langerhans.

(c) Example answer:
The strong stomach walls roll and churn the food around. They also mix in gastric juice containing the enzyme gastric protease and hydrochloric acid from the gastric glands, to produce a paste-like material called chyme. The epithelial lining of the stomach contains goblet cells which produce thick mucus to protect the stomach lining from acid erosion.

11 (a) Absorption
(b) Egestion

12 Example answer:
'Deamination' is the process by which amino acids are broken down, if there is an excess of dietary protein, by removing an amino group from the amino acid.

13 (a) Example content may include:
- Enzymes are chemicals, whereas micro-organisms are very small living organisms, such as bacteria.
- Enzymes are biological catalysts that enable the breakdown or construction of other chemicals, but they remain unchanged themselves at the end of the reactions or tasks.
- Micro-organisms do a variety of tasks, such as releasing nutrients, manufacturing vitamins and attacking pathogens.

(b) Example content may include:
- Hepatitis is inflammation of the liver and can be caused by viruses or chemical substances, including alcohol.
- The symptoms of hepatitis may include nausea, vomiting, lack of appetite and jaundice (a yellowing of the skin and whites of the eyes), and passing of dark brown urine.
- Treatment is usually rest, good nourishment and avoiding alcohol.
- In severe cases, the individual may have liver failure and require a liver transplant.

Questions 14–16: The male and female reproductive systems (pages 90–94)

14 Urethra = C
Prostate gland = H

15 Example answer:
The graph shows that mortality rates increased steadily between 1971 and 1992, reaching a peak of 30.7 per 100,000 of the population before declining gradually between 1992 and 2010. This, along with the sharp rise in the incidence of prostate cancer in the early part of the 1990s (suggesting that more men were diagnosed early enough to have life-saving treatment), supports the conclusion that increased incidence reflects improvements in diagnosis using prostate-specific antigen (PSA) testing.

16 (a) Progesterone = Y
FSH = X
Oestrogen = Z
LH = W

(b) 25 units

Question 17: Human genetics (pages 94–95)

17 Answer content could include:

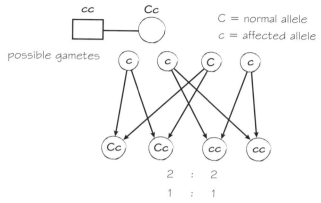

- A (affected) must be cc as the gene for cystic fibrosis is recessive.
- B must be Cc as A and B have both affected (cc) and unaffected (Cc) children.
- Parents A and B can only have children of these two genotypes (they cannot have children with CC genotype). They can have children in the ratio of 2Cc:2cc, or 1:1.
- There is a 50% chance of a child of D's genotype, Cc, being born to A and B.

Unit 4: Enquiries into Current Research in Health and Social Care

Revision task 1 (guided) (pages 97–128)

Plan for effective use of time for Part A, 18 hours (page 97)

1	Read and annotate my chosen article (page 105)	
2	Familiarise myself with the article, making notes and identifying issues (page 107)	4 hrs
3	Note keywords on identified issues, in order to search for secondary research sources (page 111)	4 hrs
4	Search and note possible sources for secondary research, related to the issues in the article (page 112)	
5	Assess reliability of Secondary source 1, chosen with reference to Source, Appearance, Method, Timeliness, Applicability and Balance (SAMTAB) and the four Part B questions (page 114)	4 hrs
6	Make notes on Secondary research source 1, including methods, reliability, ethics, importance of issue, further research (e.g. proposal, timing, ethics), impact of research on practice and provision. Show how this source links to Article 1 (page 118)	
7	Assess reliability of Secondary source 2 and make notes (see 5 and 6 above) (page 127)	4 hrs
8	Organise my Part A notes to take into my Part B assessment – 6 sides of A4 for use with Questions 1–4, including a list of my secondary sources (page 127)	2 hrs

Read and annotate Article 1 (page 98)

Your own annotations.

Familiarise yourself with Article 1 (page 101)

Example notes:

1 **What was the research piece about? (e.g. what it explored, why it was important, what the study aimed to find out)**
This research piece was about exploring how well health promotion programmes were implemented in schools. The study looked at a number of interventions that had been implemented in the UK. The purpose was to find out common themes that increased chances of positive implementation and supported children in schools to make healthy choices about their lifestyles. The researchers felt this was worthwhile because of the importance of introducing health programmes early in children's lives. This could result in better chances of preventing unhealthy choices and lifestyles later in life. The research questions were to find out:
- the main features of implementation of health programmes that resulted in failure or success
- if there were any links between these features that may explain why programmes failed or succeeded
- whether schools were best placed for the implementation of programmes that addressed specific health problems.

2 **What were the key methods used in the research? (e.g. qualitative, quantitative, mixed; how they supported the reliability of the research)**
This research used a 'realist' review method. This is a qualitative approach that develops 'programme theories'. In this case, it looked at the model of intervention, possible outcomes and activities that led to the outcomes. It reviewed 22 studies to produce a framework (programme theories) to explore the different aspects of the way the intervention programmes were implemented. It also used a saturation method, using a further 41 studies until it came to the point where no new insights were becoming apparent from these studies. Theoretical saturation is an aspect used in analysing qualitative data. Here, the researcher continues to sample and analyse data until no new data appears and the ideas in the study or theory are well defined. The methods support reliable outcomes because the researchers have sampled and analysed a lot of data and used at least two different research methods (triangulation of methods) and continually come up with the same set of conclusions. The article also refers to current guidance on the issue which, when implementation advice is given, reflects the findings of this research, such as to use a 'whole school' approach to embed programmes, so the researchers are showing that their research findings are supported by other research.

3 **What were the key findings in the research? (e.g. what were the results of the study? Did they answer the research questions? What were the conclusions/importance of the issues?)**
Through reviewing the 41 studies and testing the programme theories, the researchers identified four 'programme theories' they felt led to success in school-based programmes. These findings were:
1 Preparing. If the programme was planned so it fitted with schools' existing responsibilities, and where both pupils and teachers understood the relevance and benefits, it was more likely to succeed.
2 & 3 Introducing and embedding. If the programmes were introduced and embedded to fit with the schools' values and principles, it was more likely to be successful.
4 Implementing. There was only limited evidence to support the theory but, by monitoring and adapting elements to fit the needs of the schools, the likelihood of successful intervention increased.
The researchers discuss how current guidelines for health promotion programmes in schools link with specific health issues, e.g. alcohol, physical activity, smoking. They also note how advice given reinforces the findings in this study. They recommend that the four identified programme theories should be used in future programmes to increase the chances of successful intervention.

4 **Were any recommendations/future research plans discussed? (e.g. do they recommend further research? Did any aspects of the research did not go well? Consider proposal, methods, reliability, research skills required, ethical considerations, timescales.)**
This research found that there were links between programme theories and current guidelines that provide advice for specific intervention programmes, such as those concerning alcohol, diet, obesity (NICE, 2015, 2014, 2010, 2009 (a) (b), 2008, 2007). The study suggested that, by exploring how programmes were implemented and whether they take account of the individual needs of the schools, those implementing programmes would be more effective in promoting a successful intervention. It recommends that further research should use the programme theories when planning interventions. This may help developers to tailor-make programmes that fit the needs of individual schools while retaining standardised elements. For example, a useful piece of future research might be to identify which parts of a programme are standard (appropriate and relevant to all schools,) and which could be adapted to fit the specific needs of a group of local schools. This could lead to better implementation so money isn't wasted.
There were two areas with not so much evidence – how best to embed a programme into routine practice, and make sure it sticks to the original aims – suggesting that researchers need a longer timeline for future research. Although the ethical considerations involved in the research are not mentioned, it was based on 22 studies, some funded and supported by the NIHR, which suggests the research used ethical methods and future research should likewise use ethical methods.

5 **What could be the implications/impact on my practice? (e.g. how can this type of research affect individuals in my workplace? How will it affect my own practice?)**
The research findings for this study are helpful because they show ways to successfully implement programmes in schools. They provide a framework to follow (from using the programme theories) which could be adapted to suit the needs of the school. This would have a positive impact on my practice because it would give me a good basic framework to develop any programme and tailor it to the needs of individual children in the school. It would reduce the time it would take to develop the programme and target the right children. It would also save the costs of having to bring in outside agencies to develop programmes for the school. Interventions that fit with existing school policies and responsibilities will help embed a more successful ongoing practice in the school to support children's healthy life choices and chances. For my own practice, it will help me to understand that I can use programmes like these as a guide and adapt them to fit with the individual needs identified within the school or other setting.

6 **What could be the implications/impact on service provision? (e.g. what are the wider implications on society, and on the cost and effectiveness of service providers?)**
Intervention programmes such as this would also have a positive impact on service provision. Having generic programmes (a 'one size fits all' model) that can be adapted to suit the needs of individual schools could reduce government costs of tailor-made programmes delivered by specialist staff. This could also have a longer-term positive impact, as implementing programmes earlier in children's lives and embedding them in school programmes (e.g. healthy eating with school meal provision) will have a positive impact on the future health needs of children as they become adults. It could reduce obesity, drug addiction and alcohol misuse, representing savings to health services in terms of treatment and care.

Note keywords for searching for secondary sources (page 104)

There are a number of different terms you could use to search for secondary research sources. The examples below show how inclusion of Boolean operators and use of specific terms can provide a better focus than more generic terms.

- School intervention **and** obesity
- School intervention **and** obesity **or** alcohol
- Implementing school interventions
- Interventions in schools health
- Evaluating school **health** intervention programmes

Search for and note possible sources (page 105)

Your own responses.

Complete a SAMTAB and notes on Secondary research source 1 (page 107)

Example notes and links.

1   **What the research piece is about, and importance of issues:** Looks at how the levels of obesity have risen and how these changes relate to factors such as household income and gender. It illustrates the importance of school intervention programmes to help children and parents to tackle obesity. **Relationship to Article 1:** links very well with Article 1 as it cites programmes such as the Healthy Child Programmes that have been introduced into schools.

2   **Key methods used and reliability:** quantitative, because the research aimed to identify trends, so it used data from existing records of overweight and obese children aged 2–15 years, looking at age, gender and household income for 1995–2014 and children's desire to lose weight from 2006. Children's height and weight were measured and their BMI was calculated **Relationship to Article 1:** Article 1 used qualitative methods, because the research aimed to find out what factors affected the successful implementation of health promotion programmes in schools, including preventing excess weight gain. It used 22 UK-based studies and reviewed a further 41 studies to test the conclusions, showing four 'programme theories' that led to success in school-based programmes, to do with preparing, introducing, embedding and implementing.

3   **Key findings and importance:** There appears to have been a significant rise in obesity since 1995. Although it seems to have levelled out between 2004/5 and 2014, it is still higher than in 1995. There appears to have been little increase since 2004/5, which seems to be similar to the results of other studies in England and other high-income countries. The study suggests that obesity levels may stabilise. **Relationship to Article 1:** The levelling off suggests that the programmes of intervention discussed in Article 1 may be working. Further study into more effective programmes may reduce levels further.

4   **Recommendations/further research, also in relation to Article 1:** Plan research on successful intervention programmes to reduce obesity, matched to framework of 'programmes' in Article 1. Consider project proposal, plan/timing, methods and skills needed, and ethical considerations. To help inform this, research most recent UK data on obesity.

5   **Implications for practice and provision:** Schools need to embed programmes locally and adopt supportive practice and provision. Involvement of parents when implementing health programmes to tackle issues such as obesity could be important, as the study shows that some parents do not identify that their child is overweight or obese, or underestimate their child's weight. **Relationship to Article 1:** Article 1 also makes recommendations about factors that affect effective implementation of programmes, looking at pupils and teachers, though not parents.

Make notes on Secondary research source 1 (page 110)

4   **Were any recommendations/future research plans discussed? (e.g. do they recommend further research? Did any aspects of the research not go well? Consider proposal, methods, reliability, research skills required, ethical considerations, timescales.)**
Continuation of notes might include:
Types of method and reliability
- Research further data with an increased sample size for further analysis and evaluation for reliable findings.
- Continue with the quantitative approach but introduce some qualitative methods, for example, in research with parents.
- Your own responses for choice of quantitative/qualitative methods matched to purposes.

Relationship to Article 1
- Use the data from the secondary research source to inform research on successful intervention programmes to reduce obesity, using the framework of 'programmes' in Article 1.
- Your own responses for details of the research plan.

Limitations in current research to address in future research
- Extend research into parents' attitudes towards monitoring their children's weight and their ability to help their children learn to control their food choices.
- Your own responses for details of the research plan.

Planning
Your own suggestions for planning research, which should take into account: ethical considerations, safeguarding issues, informed consent using appropriate methods for adults and children, confidentiality and data protection, research skills required (those you have and those you need); possible problems and how to overcome them; timeline for research taking into account holidays, illness, etc.; timeline and framework for the research, e.g. updated research figures, trends and predictions for 2020.

Research literature
Your own suggestions for a literature review that might include the guidelines noted in relation to obesity and intervention, and updated research, data and predictions on obesity levels and the implications for future research, practice and provision.

5   **What could be the implications/impact on my practice? (e.g. how can this type of research affect individuals in my workplace? How will it affect my own practice?)**
Your own notes, as appropriate for your setting and practice.

6   **What could be the implications/impact on service provision? (e.g. what are the wider implications on society and on the cost and effectiveness of service providers?)**
Your own notes.

Complete a SAMTAB and notes on Secondary research source 2 (page 114)

Your own notes as appropriate for your chosen Secondary research source 2.

Part B (pages 119–128)

Article 1: How to successfully implement a school-based health promotion programme (page 119)

Your own response, based on chosen sources.

1   Continuation of answer might include:
Quantitative methods used in Secondary source 1:
- The source does not state directly what methods the researchers used, but from the methods section it seems that they reviewed data collected from a number of sources (e.g. research articles, government surveys and other surveys on the levels of obesity in England). The sources chosen by the author therefore appear reliable.
- The methods used look at existing data, statistics and research on the prevalence of obesity, its definitions, and issues surrounding obesity in England.

- It presented findings obtained using quantitative methods by giving percentages of the numbers of children considered to be obese and overweight and breaking the data down to show how the levels of obesity differed in relation to household income and gender of the children. For example, the study found that 17% of children were obese and 14% were overweight.
- One issue noted as affecting results was the need for increased data.

Research methods used in Secondary source 2:
- Your own response, based on chosen sources.

Conclusion:
- Your own response, based on chosen sources.

2 Continuation of answer might include:
- Reference to the explanations in the conclusions to Article 1 on why the issue is important.

- How the research issue may affect individuals (service users, self, colleagues) and whether it is supported by any of the research findings.
- How findings of the secondary sources link to Article 1 and whether there are any similarities that support the findings in Article 1 and indicate the importance of such programmes for individuals.
- Reference to examples, such as how the programmes might help some children to stop smoking, which might reduce future related health issues such as cancer.

3 Your own response, based on chosen sources.
4 Your own response, based on chosen sources.

Revision task 2 (page 129–141)

Your own response, based on chosen sources related to the provided article, on ways of keeping people with Alzheimer's out of care homes.